College Accounting

Fifth Edition

WORKING PAPERS 1–15

College Accounting

Fifth Edition

Douglas J. McQuaig
Wenatchee Valley College

Patricia A. Bille
Highline Community College

Houghton Mifflin Company   Boston   Toronto

Dallas   Geneva, Illinois   Palo Alto   Princeton, New Jersey

Senior Sponsoring Editor: Donald J. Golini
Senior Development Editor: Jane Sherman
Senior Project Editor: Linda Hamilton
Production Coordinator: Frances Sharperson
Manufacturing Coordinator: Sharon Pearson
Marketing Manager: Karen Natale

Cover image by The Image Bank/Paul Silverman

Printed in the U.S.A.

Library of Congress Catalog Card No.: 92-72384

ISBN: 0-395-63851-8

2 3 4 5 6 7 8 9-WC-96 95 94 93

Contents

To the Student

As you study *College Accounting*, Fifth Edition, you will find these Working Papers helpful in many different ways.

The first part of the book is a brief Review of Business Mathematics. Studying it will help you if your math skills are rusty. Next you will find a Review of T Account Placement and Representative Transactions for Chapters 1–6, 7–10, and 11–15. These reviews will help you visualize the accounts presented in your textbook and their relation to the fundamental accounting equation. Make sure you know the classification of each account presented and understand the representative transactions. Refer to these charts as you complete your homework assignments.

Then, for each chapter in the textbook, the Working Papers provide the following.

- **Learning Objectives and Key Terms** The Learning Objectives duplicate your textbook. When you begin your study session, read the objectives here and try to recall the text explanations. If you do not feel you can fulfill a learning objective, look for the learning objective in the margin of your textbook and review that material before trying to complete your homework assignments. Use the list of key terms to test your recall of vocabulary in the end-of-chapter glossaries. Look in the glossary at the end of the chapter in your textbook to find the definition of any term you do not know. If you still don't understand the term, look for the term itself in the body of the chapter. Each key term is printed in red when it is first used and defined. Make sure you understand all the key terms before going on to the next chapter.

- **Study Guide Questions** After you read each chapter in the textbook, try answering these short questions. They will show how well you have learned the material in the text. Answers are provided at the back of the Working Papers, so you can find out right away whether you are correct. If you missed a few questions, go back to the text and review those areas where your understanding is incomplete. If you have mastered the material, you are ready to go ahead.

- **Demonstration Problem and Solution** Important concepts are illustrated by a self-study problem and its solution. Test yourself by working this sample problem. Next, verify your answer with the solution presented. Also, as you work your homework assignments, you may want to refer to the Demonstration Problem as well as the text.

- **Accounting Forms** Blank forms are provided for every problem in the textbook. Sometimes information is provided to help you get started. The pages are perforated so that you can tear them out if the instructor asks for them. The wide accounting forms needed for some of the problems are at the end of the Working Papers on foldout pages. Reference is made to them at appropriate points in the regular forms.

- **Blank Forms** A selection of blank forms is provided for you to use to solve supplemental problems. If you photocopy these forms as you need them, you will not run out of forms.

After the last chapter in the Working Papers, you will find the Answers to the Study Guide Questions. The answers are followed by Check Figures for Problems. This list gives a key part of the solution for nearly every problem. You will still need to work out the full solution, but the check figure will help you stay on the right track.

We hope that the Working Papers make it easier for you to learn the fundamentals of accounting. Please write to us in care of Houghton Mifflin if you have suggestions about the text or other learning materials in your course.

Good luck in College Accounting!

Douglas J. McQuaig
Patricia A. Bille

Review of Business Mathematics

People assume that anyone who is an accountant is good at mathematics. But accountants are like anyone else; they can make simple errors in arithmetic that cause them hours of searching later on. The thing that slows down the beginning accountant more than any other single factor is not being really sure about certain common mathematical processes. For example, how do you convert from fractions to percentages? What do you do with the decimal point when you are dividing?

Of course, we all agree that an electronic calculator capable of performing the arithmetic functions is an invaluable aid in accounting. However, even with a calculator, you still need to know what to divide by what, what to multiply by what, and so forth. The calculator will do only what you tell it to do. So you will always need a knowledge of basic business mathematics.

The following short review of business mathematics, which has items labeled so that you can better identify them, is designed to help you recall what you learned about mathematics long ago. In other words, it's a mathematical booster shot.

DECIMALS

Examples of terms:

Whole number	12
Decimal	.62
Mixed decimal	4.15

Addition

When adding decimals or mixed decimals, keep the decimal points lined up, one under the other. Fill in any blank places to the right with zeros so that all the addends have the same number of decimal places.

Example   Add 4.2, 16.53, .004, and 322.

$$
\left.
\begin{array}{r}
4.200 \\
16.530 \\
.004 \\
+\ 322.000
\end{array}
\right\} \text{Addends}
$$
$$
\overline{342.734}
$$

Example   Add 16.02, 4.035, 40, and .06.

$$
\begin{array}{r}
16.020 \\
4.035 \\
40.000 \\
+\ \ \ .060 \\
\hline
60.115
\end{array}
$$

Subtraction

When subtracting decimals or mixed decimals, keep the decimal points lined up, one under the other. Fill in any blank places to the right with zeros so that all the numbers have the same number of decimal places.

Example   5.378 minus .8421.

$$
\begin{array}{r}
5.3780 \quad \text{Minuend} \\
-\ .8421 \quad \text{Subtrahend} \\
\hline
4.5359
\end{array}
$$

Example   624.1 minus 16.003.

$$
\begin{array}{r}
624.100 \\
-\ 16.003 \\
\hline
608.097
\end{array}
$$

Multiplication

When multiplying decimals or mixed decimals, find the position of the decimal point in the product (answer) by adding the number of decimal places in the multiplicand (number to be multiplied) and in the multiplier (number of times to multiply), and count off the same number of places from right to left in the product.

Example   Multiply .62 by .4.

$$
\begin{array}{r}
.62 \quad \text{Multiplicand} \\
\times\ .4 \quad \text{Multiplier} \\
\hline
.248 \quad \text{Product}
\end{array}
$$

Example   Multiply 626.231 by 2.87.

$$
\begin{array}{r}
626.231 \\
\times\ 2.87 \\
\hline
43\,83617 \\
500\,9848 \\
1\,252\,462 \\
\hline
1,797.28297
\end{array}
$$

When the number of decimal places required is greater than the number of places in the product, add as many zeros to the left of the product as necessary.

Example   Multiply .049 by .02.

$$
\begin{array}{r}
.049 \\
\times\ .02 \\
\hline
.00098
\end{array}
$$

Example   Multiply .26 by .0091.

$$
\begin{array}{r}
.26 \\
\times\ .0091 \\
\hline
26 \\
234 \\
\hline
.002366
\end{array}
$$

Division

When the divisor (dividing number) is a whole number and the dividend (number to be divided) is a mixed decimal, place the decimal point in the quotient (answer) directly above the decimal point in the dividend.

Example Divide 172.64 by 4.

$$
\begin{array}{r}
43.16 \quad \text{Quotient} \\
\text{Divisor} \quad 4)\overline{172.64} \quad \text{Dividend} \\
\underline{16} \\
12 \\
\underline{12} \\
6 \\
\underline{4} \\
24 \\
\underline{24}
\end{array}
$$

Example Divide 6.39 by 15.

$$
\begin{array}{r}
.426 \\
15)\overline{6.390} \\
\underline{6\,0} \\
39 \\
\underline{30} \\
90 \\
\underline{90}
\end{array}
$$

When the divisor is a decimal, move the decimal point in the divisor as many places to the right as necessary to make the divisor a whole number, and move the decimal point in the dividend to the right also, the same number of places.

Example Divide 14.406 by .007.

$$
\begin{array}{r}
2\,058. \\
.007)\overline{14.406} \\
\underline{14} \\
40 \\
\underline{35} \\
56 \\
\underline{56}
\end{array}
$$

Example Divide 8.3927 by .943.

$$
\begin{array}{r}
8.9 \\
.943)\overline{8.3927} \\
\underline{7\,544} \\
8487 \\
8487
\end{array}
$$

FRACTIONS

Examples of terms:

$$\frac{\text{Numerator} \longrightarrow 6}{\text{Denominator} \longrightarrow 39}$$

Proper fraction 8/9
Improper fraction 13/6
Mixed number 2⅜
Like fractions 2/5, 3/5, 4/5
Unlike fractions 1/2, 1/4, 5/6

Addition

To add like fractions, add their numerators.

Example Add 1/5 and 3/5.

$$\begin{array}{r} 1/5 \\ + 3/5 \\ \hline 4/5 \end{array}$$

To add unlike fractions, you must convert them to like fractions. First, find the least common denominator (the smallest number that is exactly divisible by each denominator).

Next, divide the least common denominator by the denominator of each original fraction. Then multiply both the numerator and the denominator of each original fraction by this number. Add the numerators of the like fractions and, if necessary, reduce the sum of lowest terms.

Example Add 3/4 and 2/3. The least common denominator is 12.

$$4\overline{)12} \quad \frac{3}{4} = \frac{3 \times 3}{4 \times 3} = \frac{9}{12}$$
$$3\overline{)12} \quad \frac{2}{3} = \frac{2 \times 4}{3 \times 4} = +\frac{8}{12}$$
$$\frac{17}{12} = 1\frac{5}{12}$$

Example Add 1/3, 1/6, and 3/8. The least common denominator is 24.

$$3\overline{)24} \quad \frac{1}{3} = \frac{1 \times 8}{3 \times 8} = \frac{8}{24}$$
$$6\overline{)24} \quad \frac{1}{6} = \frac{1 \times 4}{6 \times 4} = \frac{4}{24}$$
$$8\overline{)24} \quad \frac{3}{8} = \frac{3 \times 3}{8 \times 3} = +\frac{9}{24}$$
$$\frac{21}{24} = \frac{7}{8}$$

Subtraction

To subtract like fractions, subtract their numerators.

Example   7/8 minus 3/8.

$$\begin{array}{r} 7/8 \\ -\ 3/8 \\ \hline 4/8 = 1/2 \end{array}$$

To subtract unlike fractions, you must convert them to like fractions. First, find the least common denominator and divide it by the denominator of each original fraction. Then multiply both the numerator and the denominator of each original fraction by this number and subtract. When subtracting mixed numbers, change each mixed number to an improper like fraction.

Example   8/9 minus 5/12. The common denominator is 36.

$$9\overline{)36}^{\,4} \qquad \frac{8}{9} = \frac{8 \times 4}{9 \times 4} = \frac{32}{36}$$
$$12\overline{)36}^{\,3} \qquad \frac{5}{12} = \frac{5 \times 3}{12 \times 3} = -\frac{15}{36}$$
$$\frac{17}{36}$$

Example   4 1/6 minus 2 3/8. The common denominator is 24.

$$6\overline{)24}^{\,4} \qquad 4\frac{1}{6} = \frac{25 \times 4}{6 \times 4} = \frac{100}{24}$$
$$8\overline{)24}^{\,3} \qquad 2\frac{3}{8} = \frac{19 \times 3}{8 \times 3} = -\frac{57}{24}$$
$$\frac{43}{24} = 1\frac{19}{24}$$

Multiplication

When multiplying fractions, first simplify by canceling (dividing one numerator and one denominator, regardless of their positions, by the same number). Next multiply the numerators, multiply the denominators, and reduce the results to the lowest terms.

Example   5/16 × 1/5 × 9/8.

$$\frac{\overset{1}{\cancel{5}}}{16} \times \frac{1}{\cancel{5}} \times \frac{9}{8} = \frac{1 \times 1 \times 9}{16 \times 1 \times 8} = \frac{9}{128}$$

Example   140 × 4/25 × 5/18.

$$\frac{\overset{14}{\cancel{\overset{28}{\cancel{140}}}}}{1} \times \frac{4}{\cancel{25}} \times \frac{\cancel{5}}{\cancel{18}} = \frac{14 \times 4 \times 1}{1 \times 1 \times 9} = \frac{56}{9} = 6\frac{2}{9}$$

Division

When dividing fractions, invert the divisor (turn the fraction upside down) and multiply.

Example   Divide 7/16 by 3/4.

$$\frac{7}{16} \div \frac{3}{4} = \frac{7}{\cancel{16}_{\,4}} \times \frac{\cancel{4}^{\,1}}{3} = \frac{7 \times 1}{4 \times 3} = \frac{7}{12}$$

Example   Divide 36 by 2/3.

$$36 \div \frac{2}{3} = \frac{\cancel{36}^{\,18}}{1} \times \frac{3}{\cancel{2}_{\,1}} = 54$$

Changing a Fraction to a Decimal

Divide the numerator by the denominator.

Example   Change 7/8 to a decimal.

```
      .875
  8)7.000
    6 4
    ─────
      60
      56
    ─────
      40
      40
    ─────
```

Example   Change 146/42 to a decimal.

$$\frac{146}{42} = \frac{146 \div 2}{42 \div 2} = \frac{73}{21}$$

```
       3.476+
   21)73.000
      63
     ──────
      10 0
       8 4
     ──────
       1 60
       1 47
     ──────
        130
        126
      ──────
          4
```

Changing a Decimal to a Fraction

Draw a line under the decimal. Write a 1 immediately below the decimal point and a 0 below each number in the decimal. Then drop the decimal point. Reduce to lowest terms.

Example   Change .72 to a fraction.

$$.72 = \frac{72}{100} = \frac{72 \div 4}{100 \div 4} = \frac{18}{25}$$

Example   Change .8125 to a fraction.

$$.8125 = \frac{8125}{10,000} = \frac{8125 \div 625}{10,000 \div 625} = \frac{13}{16}$$

Common Decimal Equivalents

The following equivalents are rounded off at the fourth decimal place.

$\frac{1}{2} = .5$ $\frac{1}{6} = .1667$ $\frac{1}{10} = .1$

$\frac{1}{3} = .3333$ $\frac{1}{7} = .1429$ $\frac{1}{11} = .0909$

$\frac{2}{3} = .6667$ $\frac{1}{8} = .125$ $\frac{1}{12} = .0833$

$\frac{1}{4} = .25$ $\frac{3}{8} = .375$ $\frac{1}{15} = .0667$

$\frac{3}{4} = .75$ $\frac{5}{8} = .625$ $\frac{1}{16} = .0625$

$\frac{1}{5} = .2$ $\frac{7}{8} = .875$ $\frac{1}{20} = .05$

$\frac{3}{5} = .6$ $\frac{1}{9} = .1111$ $\frac{1}{25} = .04$

PERCENTAGES

Percentages are fractions that have 100 for their denominators.

Changing a Percentage to a Decimal

Drop the percent sign and move the decimal point two places to the left. If the percentage consists of only one digit, add a 0 to the left of the digit.

Example   Change 36 percent to a decimal.

$36\% = 36. = .36$

Example   Change 5.85 percent to a decimal.

$5.85\% = 05.85 = .0585$

Changing a Decimal to a Percentage

Move the decimal point two places to the right and add the percent sign.

Example   Change .48 to a percentage.

$.48 = .48 = 48\%$

Example   Change 1.495 to a percentage.

$1.495 = 1.495 = 149.5\%$

Changing a Percentage to a Fraction

Drop the percent sign, make a fraction with the percentage as numerator and 100 as denominator, and reduce to lowest terms.

Example   Change 25 percent to a fraction.

$$25\% = \frac{25}{100} = \frac{25 \div 25}{100 \div 25} = \frac{1}{4}$$

Example   Change 31.5% to a fraction.

$$31.5\% = \frac{31.5}{100} = \frac{315}{1,000} = \frac{315 \div 5}{1,000 \div 5} = \frac{63}{200}$$

Changing a Fraction to a Percentage

Reduce to lowest terms. Divide the numerator by the denominator and move the decimal point two places to the right and add the percent sign.

Example   Change 5/8 to a percentage.

$$.625 = .62.5 = 62.5\%$$

```
  .625
8)5.000
  4 8
    20
    16
    40
    40
```

Example   Change 46/8 to a percentage.

$$\frac{46}{8} = \frac{46 \div 2}{8 \div 2} = \frac{23}{4}$$

$$5.75 = 5.75 = 575\%$$

```
   5.75
4)23.00
  20
   3 0
   2 8
     20
     20
```

Finding the Ratio of . . . to . . .

This is the same thing as finding the percentage that one thing is of another. Write the "of . . ." amount in the numerator and the "to . . ." amount in the denominator. Reduce to lowest terms and divide the numerator by the denominator. Put a colon and the number 1 to the right of the answer.

Example Find the ratio of current assets ($69,000) to current liabilities ($27,000).

$$\frac{69{,}000}{27{,}000} = \frac{69{,}000 \div 3{,}000}{27{,}000 \div 3{,}000} = \frac{23}{9}$$

$$2.555 = 2.555 \text{ or } 2.56 = 2.56{:}1$$

```
     2.555
9)23.000
   18
    5 0
    4 5
      50
      45
      50
      45
       5
```

Example Find the ratio of salesroom floor space (6,000 square feet) to office floor space (900 square feet).

$$\frac{6{,}000}{900} = \frac{6{,}000 \div 300}{900 \div 300} = \frac{20}{3}$$

$$6.666 = 6.666 \text{ or } 6.67 = 6.67{:}1$$

```
     6.666
3)20.000
   18
    2 0
    1 8
      20
      18
      20
      18
       2
```

Finding the Percentage of Increase or Decrease

Divide the amount of the change by the base (starting figure). Change the decimal to a percentage

Example Moore's income increased from $12,000 to $15,000. Find the percentage of increase.

Amount of change = 15,000 − 12,000 = 3,000

$$= .25 = 25\%$$

```
          .25
12,000)3,000.00
       2 400 0
         600 00
         600 00
```

Example Arnold's grade-point average decreased from 3.6 to 3.1. Find the percentage of decrease.

Amount of change = 3.6 − 3.1 = .5
= .1388 or .139 = 13.9%

$$
\begin{array}{r}
.1388 \\
3.6\overline{)5.0000} \\
3\,6 \\
\hline
1\,40 \\
1\,08 \\
\hline
320 \\
288 \\
\hline
320 \\
288 \\
\hline
32
\end{array}
$$

ROUNDING OFF

If the last number in a decimal is 5 or greater, drop it and add one to the next number on the left. If the last number in a decimal is less than 5, drop it and let the other number stay the same.

Example Round off to two decimal places.

1.825 = 1.83

Example Round off to three decimal places.

.6923 = .692

Review of T Account Placement and Representative Transactions:

CHAPTERS 1 THROUGH 6

Review of T Account Placement

The following display sums up the placement of T accounts covered in Chapters 2 through 6 in relation to the fundamental accounting equation. Italicized accounts are contra accounts.

Assets	=	Liabilities	+	Owner's Equity	+	Revenue	−	Expenses
+ | −		− | +		− | +		− | +		+ | −
Debit | Credit		Debit | Credit		Debit | Credit		Debit | Credit		Debit | Credit

Cash	Accounts Payable	J. R. Doe, Capital	Income from Services	Rent Expense
+ | −	− | +	− | +	− | +	+ | −

Accounts Receivable	Wages Payable	*J. R. Doe, Drawing*	Professional Fees	Wages Expense
+ | −	− | +	+ | −	− | +	+ | −

Supplies		Income Summary	Commissions Earned	Advertising Expense
+ | −		Expense | Revenue	− | +	+ | −

Prepaid Insurance	Utilities Expense
+ | −	+ | −

Equipment	Supplies Expense
+ | −	+ | −

Accumulated Depreciation, Equipment	Insurance Expense
− | +	+ | −

Depreciation Expense, Equipment
+ | −

Review of Representative Transactions

The following table summarizes the recording of the various transactions described in Chapters 1–6 and the classification of the accounts involved.

Transaction	Accounts Involved	Class.	Increase or Decrease	Therefore Debit or Credit	Financial Statement
Owner invested cash in business	Cash	A	I	Debit	Balance Sheet
	J. R. Doe, Capital	OE	I	Credit	Statement of Owner's Equity
Bought equipment for cash	Equipment	A	I	Debit	Balance Sheet
	Cash	A	D	Credit	Balance Sheet
Bought supplies on account	Supplies	A	I	Debit	Balance Sheet
	Accounts Payable	L	I	Credit	Balance Sheet
Bought equipment paying a down payment with the remainder on account	Equipment	A	I	Debit	Balance Sheet
	Cash	A	D	Credit	Balance Sheet
	Accounts Payable	L	I	Credit	Balance Sheet
Paid premium for insurance policy	Prepaid Insurance	A	I	Debit	Balance Sheet
	Cash	A	D	Credit	Balance Sheet
Paid creditor on account	Accounts Payable	L	D	Debit	Balance Sheet
	Cash	A	D	Credit	Balance Sheet
Sold services for cash	Cash	A	I	Debit	Balance Sheet
	Income from Services	R	I	Credit	Income State.
Paid rent for month	Rent Expense	E	I	Debit	Income State.
	Cash	A	D	Credit	Balance Sheet
Billed customers for services performed	Accounts Receivable	A	I	Debit	Balance Sheet
	Income from Services	R	I	Credit	Income State.
Owner withdrew cash for personal use	J. R. Doe, Drawing	OE	I	Debit	Statement of Owner's Equity
	Cash	A	D	Credit	Balance Sheet

Transaction	Accounts Involved	Class.	Increase or Decrease	Therefore Debit or Credit	Financial Statement
Received cash from charge customers to apply on account	Cash Accounts Receivable	A A	I D	Debit Credit	Balance Sheet Balance Sheet
Paid wages to employees	Wages Expense Cash	E A	I D	Debit Credit	Income State. Balance Sheet
Adjusting entry for supplies used	Supplies Expense Supplies	E A	I D	Debit Credit	Income State. Balance Sheet
Adjusting entry for insurance expired	Insurance Expense Prepaid Insurance	E A	I D	Debit Credit	Income State. Balance Sheet
Adjusting entry for depreciation of assets	Depreciation Expense Accumulated Depreciation	E A	I I	Debit Credit	Income State. Balance Sheet
Adjusting entry for accrued wages	Wages Expense Wages Payable	E L	I I	Debit Credit	Income State. Balance Sheet
Closing entry for revenue accounts	Revenue accounts Income Summary	R OE	D —	Debit Credit	Income State. —
Closing entry for expense accounts	Income Summary Expense accounts	OE E	— D	Debit Credit	— Income State.
Closing entry for Income Summary account (Net Income)	Income Summary J. R. Doe, Capital	OE OE	— I	Debit Credit	— Balance Sheet
Closing entry for Drawing account	J. R. Doe, Capital J. R. Doe, Drawing	OE OE	D D	Debit Credit	Balance Sheet State. of Owner's Equity

Review of T Account Placement

The following sums up the placement of T accounts covered in Chapters 7 through 10 in relation to the fundamental accounting equation.

Assets			Liabilities			Owner's Equity			Revenue			Expenses
+	**−**	**=**	**−**	**+**	**+**	**−**	**+**	**+**	**−**	**+**	**−**	**+**
Debit	Credit		Debit	Credit		Debit	Credit		Debit	Credit		Debit	Credit

Petty Cash Fund

+	−

Change Fund

+	−

Notes Receivable

+	−

Prepaid Workers' Compensation Insurance

+	−

Unearned Rent

−	+

FICA Tax Payable

−	+

Employees' Income Tax Payable

−	+

Employees' Bond Deduction Payable

−	+

Employees' Union Dues Payable

−	+

Employees' Medical Insurance Payable

−	+

Federal Unemployment Tax Payable

−	+

State Unemployment Tax Payable

−	+

Rent Income

−	+

Interest Income

−	+

Cash Short and Over

	Credit balance

Payroll Tax Expense

+	−

Workers' Compensation Insurance Expense

+	−

Cash Short and Over

Debit balance	

Review of Representative Transactions

The following summarizes the recording of transactions covered in Chapters 7 through 10, along with a classification of the accounts involved.

Transaction	Accounts Involved	Class.	Increase or Decrease	Therefore Debit or Credit	Financial Statement
Established a Petty Cash Fund	Petty Cash Fund	A	I	Debit	Balance Sheet
	Cash	A	D	Credit	Balance Sheet
Reimbursed Petty Cash Fund	Expenses or	E	I	Debit	Income State.
	Assets or	A		Debit	Balance Sheet
	Drawing	OE		Debit	State. of O.E.
	Cash	A	D	Credit	Balance Sheet
Established a Change Fund	Change Fund	A	I	Debit	Balance Sheet
	Cash	A	D	Credit	Balance Sheet
Recorded cash sales (amount on cash register tape was larger than cash count)	Cash	A	I	Debit	Balance Sheet
	Cash Short and Over	E	—	Debit	Income State.
	Sales	R	I	Credit	Income State.
Recorded cash sales (amount on cash register tape was less than cash count)	Cash	A	I	Debit	Balance Sheet
	Sales	R	I	Credit	Income State.
	Cash Short and Over	R	—	Credit	Income State.
Recorded service charges on bank account	Miscellaneous Expense	E	I	Debit	Income State.
	Cash	A	D	Credit	Balance Sheet
Recorded NSF check received from customer	Accounts Receivable	A	I	Debit	Balance Sheet
	Cash	A	D	Credit	Balance Sheet
Recorded interest-bearing note receivable collected by our bank	Cash	A	I	Debit	Balance Sheet
	Notes Receivable	A	D	Credit	Balance Sheet
	Interest Income	R	I	Credit	Income State.

Transaction	Accounts Involved	Class.	Increase or Decrease	Therefore Debit or Credit	Financial Statement
Recorded the payroll entry from the payroll register	Sales Salary Expense	E	I	Debit	Income State.
	Office Salary Expense	E	I	Debit	Income State.
	FICA Tax Payable	L	I	Credit	Balance Sheet
	Employees' Income Tax Payable	L	I	Credit	Balance Sheet
	Employees' Bond Deduction Payable	L	I	Credit	Balance Sheet
	Employees' Union Dues Payable	L	I	Credit	Balance Sheet
	Salaries Payable	L	I	Credit	Balance Sheet
Issued check payable to payroll bank account	Salaries Payable	L	D	Debit	Balance Sheet
	Cash	A	D	Credit	Balance Sheet
Recorded employer's payroll taxes	Payroll Tax Expense	E	I	Debit	Income State.
	FICA Tax Payable	L	I	Credit	Balance Sheet
	State Unemployment Tax Payable	L	I	Credit	Balance Sheet
	Federal Unemployment Tax Payable	L	I	Credit	Balance Sheet
Recorded deposit of FICA taxes and employees' income tax withheld	Employee's Income Tax Payable	L	D	Debit	Balance Sheet
	FICA Tax Payable	L	D	Debit	Balance Sheet
	Cash	A	D	Credit	Balance Sheet
Recorded deposit of federal unemployment tax	Federal Unemployment Tax Payable	L	D	Debit	Balance Sheet
	Cash	A	D	Credit	Balance Sheet
Paid state unemployment tax	State Unemployment Tax Payable	L	D	Debit	Balance Sheet
	Cash	A	D	Credit	Balance Sheet
Paid for workers' compensation insurance in advance	Prepaid Workers' Compensation Insurance	A	I	Debit	Balance Sheet
	Cash	A	D	Credit	Balance Sheet
Adjusting entry for workers' compensation insurance, assuming an additional amount is owed	Workers' Compensation Insurance Expense	E	I	Debit	Income State.
	Prepaid Workers' Compensation Insurance	A	D	Credit	Balance Sheet
	Workers' Compensation Insurance Payable	L	I	Credit	Balance Sheet

Review of T Account Placement

The following sums up the placement of T accounts covered in Chapters 11 through 15 in relation to the fundamental accounting equation. Italics indicates those accounts that are treated as deductions from the related accounts above them.

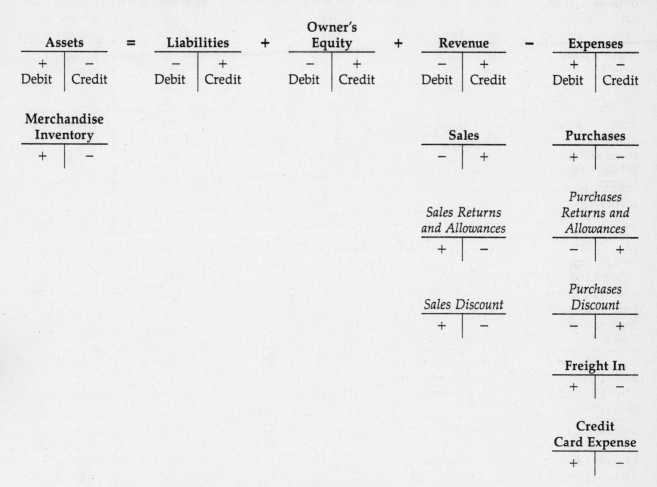

Review of Representative Transactions

The following table summarizes the recording of transactions covered in Chapters 11 through 15, along with a classification of the accounts involved.

Classifications

Balance Sheet		Income Statement	
CA	Current Assets	S	Revenue from Sales
P & E	Plant and Equipment	CGS	Cost of Goods Sold
CL	Current Liabilities	SE	Selling Expenses
LTL	Long-Term Liabilities	GE	General Expenses
		OI	Other Income
		OE	Other Expenses

Transaction	Accounts Involved	Class.	Increase or Decrease	Therefore Debit or Credit	Financial Statement
Sold merchandise on account	Accounts Receivable	CA	I	Debit	Balance Sheet
	Sales	S	I	Credit	Income State.
Sold merchandise on account involving sales tax	Accounts Receivable	CA	I	Debit	Balance Sheet
	Sales	S	I	Credit	Income State.
	Sales Tax Payable	CL	I	Credit	Balance Sheet
Issued credit memo to customer for merchandise returned	Sales Returns and Allowances	S	I	Debit	Income State.
	Accounts Receivable	CA	D	Credit	Balance Sheet
Summarizing entry for the total of sales invoices for sales on account for the month	Accounts Receivable	CA	I	Debit	Balance Sheet
	Sales	S	I	Credit	Income State.
Bought merchandise on account	Purchases	CGS	I	Debit	Income State.
	Accounts Payable	CL	I	Credit	Balance Sheet
Bought merchandise on account with freight prepaid as a convenience to the buyer	Purchases	CGS	I	Debit	Income State.
	Freight In	CGS	I	Debit	Income State.
	Accounts Payable	CL	I	Credit	Balance Sheet
Received credit memo from supplier for merchandise returned	Accounts Payable	CL	D	Debit	Balance Sheet
	Purchases Returns and Allowances	CGS	I	Credit	Income State.
Summarizing entry for the total of purchases of all types of goods on account	Purchases	CGS	I	Debit	Income State.
	Store Supplies	CA	I	Debit	Balance Sheet
	Office Supplies	CA	I	Debit	Balance Sheet
	Store Equipment	P & E	I	Debit	Balance Sheet
	Accounts Payable	CL	I	Credit	Balance Sheet
Paid for transportation charges on incoming merchandise	Freight In	CGS	I	Debit	Income State.
	Cash	CA	D	Credit	Balance Sheet
Sold merchandise, involving sales tax, for cash	Cash	CA	I	Debit	Balance Sheet
	Sales	S	I	Credit	Income State.
	Sales Tax Payable	CL	I	Credit	Balance Sheet

Transaction	Accounts Involved	Class.	Increase or Decrease	Therefore Debit or Credit	Financial Statement
Sold merchandise involving a sales tax and the customer used a bank charge card	Cash Credit Card Expense Sales Sales Tax Payable	CA SE S CL	I I I I	Debit Debit Credit Credit	Balance Sheet Income State. Income State. Balance Sheet
Charge customer paid bill within the discount period	Cash Sales Discount Accounts Receivable	CA S CA	I I D	Debit Debit Credit	Balance Sheet Income State. Balance Sheet
Paid invoice for the purchase of merchandise within the discount period	Accounts Payable Cash Purchases Discount	CL CA CGS	D D I	Debit Credit Credit	Balance Sheet Balance Sheet Income State.
First adjusting entry for merchandise inventory	Income Summary Merchandise Inventory	— CA & CGS	— D	Debit Credit	— Balance Sheet & Income State.
Second adjusting entry for merchandise inventory	Merchandise Inventory Income Summary	CA & CGS —	I —	Debit Credit	Balance Sheet & Income State.
Adjusting entry for rent earned (Rent Income)	Unearned Rent Rent Income	CL OI	D I	Debit Credit	Balance Sheet Income State.
Reversing entry for adjustment for accrued wages	Wages Payable Wages Expense	CL SE or GE	D D	Debit Credit	Balance Sheet Income State.

College Accounting

Fifth Edition

1 | Analyzing Business Transactions: Asset, Liability, and Owner's Equity Accounts

LEARNING OBJECTIVES

1. Define accounting.
2. Describe the duties of an accounting clerk, a general bookkeeper, and an accountant.
3. Define and identify asset, liability, and owner's equity accounts.
4. Record a group of business transactions, in column form, involving changes in assets, liabilities, and owner's equity.
5. Prepare a balance sheet.

KEY TERMS

Account form
Accounting
Accounts
Accounts Payable
Assets
Balance sheet
Business entity
Capital
Certified Public Accountant (CPA)
Chart of accounts
Creditor
Double-entry accounting

Economic unit
Equity
Financial position
Fundamental accounting equation
Generally accepted accounting principles (GAAP)
Liabilities
Owner's equity
Report form
Sole proprietorship
Transaction

STUDY GUIDE QUESTIONS

PART 1 True/False

For each of the following statements, circle T if the statement is true and F if the statement is false.

T F 1. An accountant keeps a separate record for each asset, liability, and owner's equity account.

T F 2. The term *owner's equity* means the owner's investment.

T F 3. When an asset is purchased for cash, the owner's equity account is decreased.

T F 4. People who loan money to a company are considered the company's debtors.

T F 5. A business enterprise is considered an economic unit.

T F 6. Equipment and supplies are considered assets.

T F 7. There is a marked difference between bookkeeping and accounting.

T F 8. A summary of assets, liabilities, and owner's equity shows the financial position of an economic unit.

T F 9. The third line in the heading of a balance sheet indicates one specific date.

T F 10. More people are engaged in private accounting than in public accounting.

PART 2 Completion—Language of Business

Complete each of the following statements by writing the appropriate words in the spaces provided.

1. A one-owner business is called a(n) _____ .
2. Debts owed by a business are called _____ .
3. A person or business to whom money is owed is called a(n) _____ .
4. The categories listed under the headings Assets, Liabilities, and Owner's Equity are called _____ .
5. An event affecting a business that can be expressed in terms of money and that must be recorded in the accounting records is called a(n) _____ .
6. The owner's investment or equity in an enterprise is called _____ .
7. The equation expressing the relationship of assets, liabilities, and owner's equity is called the _____ .
8. The _____ is the official list of account titles to be used to record the transactions of a business.
9. In the _____ form of a balance sheet, assets are placed at the top, and the liabilities and owner's equity are placed below.
10. The financial interest in or claim to an asset is called _____ .

PART 3 Classifying Accounts

The office of financial consultant R. D. Willard has the following accounts:

Office Equipment   Mortgage Payable
Supplies   Land
Accounts Payable   R. D. Willard, Capital
Building   Prepaid Insurance
Cash   Neon Sign

List each account under the appropriate heading.

Assets	Liabilities
_____	_____
_____	_____
_____	
_____	
_____	**Owner's Equity**
_____	
_____	_____

PART 4 Completion—Balance Sheet

Complete the following balance sheet for Niemi Insurance Agency as of October 31, 19—:

_(a)_
_____

_(b)_
_____

_(c)_
_____

_(d)_			
Cash	$ 2 7 0 0 00		
Supplies	1 5 5 2 00		
Land	15 4 0 0 00		
Building	96 0 0 0 00		
Office Equipment	7 9 2 0 00		
Office Furniture	4 2 0 0 00		
_(e)_		$	_(i)_
_(f)_			
Accounts Payable	$		_(j)_
Mortgage Payable	57 0 0 0 00		
Total Liabilities		$57 9 4 0 00	
_(g)_			
B. C. Niemi, Capital			_(k)_
_(h)_		$	_(l)_

DEMONSTRATION PROBLEM

R. J. Newhouse recently established Computer Consultants. Record the following transactions using plus and minus signs:

a. Newhouse deposited $3,500 in cash at First State Bank in the name of the business.
b. Newhouse invested his personally owned computer and office equipment, having a present value of $4,000, in the business.
c. Bought office supplies on account from Bryan Office Supply, $952.
d. Bought office furniture for $3,400 from Office Furniture To Go, paying $680 down with the remainder due in thirty days.
e. Paid Bryan Office Supply $476 as part payment on account.

Instructions

1. Record the transactions and the balances after each transaction using the following headings:

Assets	=	Liabilities	+ Owner's Equity
Cash + Supplies + Equipment + Furniture		Accounts Payable	R. J. Newhouse

2. Prepare a balance sheet dated September 30 of this year.

SOLUTION

	Assets				=	Liabilities	+	Owner's Equity
	Cash	+ Supplies	+ Equipment	+ Furniture		Accounts Payable		R. J. Newhouse, Capital
(a)	+3,500							+3,500
(b)			+4,000					+4,000
Bal.	3,500 +	+	4,000 +		=		+	7,500
(c)		+952				+952		
Bal.	3,500 +	952 +	4,000 +		=	952	+	7,500
(d)	−680			+3,400		+2,720		
Bal.	2,820 +	952 +	4,000 +	3,400	=	3,672	+	7,500
(e)	−476					−476		
Bal.	2,344 +	952 +	4,000 +	3,400	=	3,196	+	7,500

Proof of Totals

Cash	$ 2,344			
Supplies	952			
Equipment	4,000	Accounts Payable	$ 3,196
Furniture	3,400	R. J. Newhouse, Capital	7,500
	$10,696		$10,696

Computer Consultants

Balance Sheet

September 30, 19—

Assets		
Cash	$2 3 4 4 00	
Supplies	9 5 2 00	
Equipment	4 0 0 0 00	
Furniture	3 4 0 0 00	
Total Assets		$10 6 9 6 00
Liabilities		
Accounts Payable		$ 3 1 9 6 00
Owner's Equity		
R. J. Newhouse, Capital		7 5 0 0 00
Total Liabilities and Owner's Equity		$10 6 9 6 00

PROBLEM 1-1A or 1-1B

	Assets			=	Liabilities	+	Owner's Equity
	Cash	+ Supplies	+ Equipment		Accounts Payable		, Capital
(a)							
(b)							
Bal.		+	+	=		+	
(c)							
Bal.		+	+	=		+	
(d)							
Bal.		+	+	=		+	
(e)							
Bal.		+	+	=		+	
(f)							
Bal.		+	+	=		+	

Proof of Totals

Cash

Supplies

Equipment _____

Accounts Payable

, Capital _____

PROBLEM 1-2A or 1-2B

PROBLEM 1-3A or 1-3B

		Assets			=	Liabilities	+	Owner's Equity
	Cash	+	Supplies	+ Equipment		Accounts Payable		, Capital
(a)								
(b)								
Bal.		+		+	=		+	
(c)								
Bal.		+		+	=		+	
(d)								
Bal.		+		+	=		+	
(e)								
Bal.		+		+	=		+	
(f)								
Bal.		+		+	=		+	
(g)								
Bal.		+		+	=		+	

Proof of Totals

Cash

Supplies

Equipment _____

Accounts Payable

, Capital _____

PROBLEM 1-4A or 1-4B

2 Analyzing Business Transactions: Revenue and Expense Accounts

LEARNING OBJECTIVES

1. Define revenue and expense.
2. Record a group of business transactions in column form, involving all five elements of the fundamental accounting equation.
3. Prepare an income statement.
4. Prepare a statement of owner's equity.
5. Prepare a statement of owner's equity when there is an additional investment with either a net income or a net loss.

KEY TERMS

Accounts Receivable
Expenses
Fair market value
Financial statement
Income statement

Net income
Net loss
Revenues
Statement of owner's equity
Withdrawal

STUDY GUIDE QUESTIONS

PART 1   True/False

For each of the following statements, circle T if the statement is true and F if the statement is false.

T   F   1. An income statement shows the financial condition of an economic unit.

T   F   2. When a business receives a payment from a charge customer, the revenue account is not affected.

T   F   3. The third line in the heading of a statement of owner's equity lists a specific date.

T   F   4. Expenses have the effect of decreasing owner's equity.

T   F   5. The net income for a given financial period is found in both the income statement and the balance sheet.

T   F   6. The amounts owed by charge customers are recorded in the Accounts Receivable account.

T   F   7. In preparing the financial statements for a business, the balance sheet should be prepared first, followed by the income statement and then the statement of owner's equity.

T   F   8. Withdrawals by the owner decrease owner's equity.

T   F   9. The net income is the connecting link between the income statement and the statement of owner's equity.

T   F   10. An income statement is prepared at the end of the financial period to show the results of operations.

PART 2 Completion—Language of Business

Complete each of the following statements by writing the appropriate word(s) in the space provided.

1. _____ represents the amount a business charges a customer for a service performed.

2. The _____ shows how the capital account has changed over the financial period.

3. If the owner takes cash out of the business each month, this is called a(n) _____ .

4. Over a period of time, if total revenue is less than total expenses, the result is a(n) _____ .

5. If an asset is invested in a business, the asset should be recorded at its _____ , or the amount that would be received if the asset were sold to an outsider on the open market.

6. The _____ shows the results of business transactions involving revenue and expense accounts over a period of time.

7. The account used to record the amounts owed by charge customers is _____ .

8. _____ are the costs related to the earning of revenue.

PART 3 Analyzing Transactions

Here are some typical transactions of Hinson Termite Control Service. For each transaction, indicate the increase (+) or the decrease (−) in Assets (A), Liabilities (L), Owner's Equity (OE), Revenue (R), or Expenses (E) by placing the appropriate sign(s) in the appropriate column(s). The first transaction is given as an example.

	A	L	OE	R	E
0. *Example:* Owner invested cash	+		+		
1. Payment of rent					
2. Sale of services for cash					
3. Investment of equipment by owner					
4. Payment of insurance premium for two years					
5. Payment of wages					
6. Sales of services on account					
7. Withdrawal of cash by owner					
8. Purchase of supplies on account					
9. Collection from charge customer previously billed					
10. Payment made to creditor on account					

PART 4 Statement of Owner's Equity

Complete the statement of owner's equity for C. P. Sebring Company for the month of June of this year. The following information is available:

Net Income for June	$ 3,400
C. P. Sebring, Capital, June 1	106,500
Withdrawals for June	3,200
Additional Investment, June 16	4,000

DEMONSTRATION PROBLEM

During November of this year, James Chin opened an accounting practice called James Chin, C.P.A. The following transactions were incurred during the first month:

a. Deposited $13,500 in a bank account in the name of James Chin, C.P.A.
b. Paid rent for the month, $1,600.
c. Bought office equipment, including a computer and a printer, for $9,500 from Bingham Company. Paid $6,700 in cash, with the balance due in 30 days.
d. Purchased office supplies and announcements for $970 from City Stationers. Payment is due in 30 days.
e. Billed clients $5,500 for services rendered (Client Fees).
f. Paid $1,450 to secretary/assistant for the month.
g. Paid telephone bill of $210 (Telephone Expense).
h. Received cash from clients previously billed on account, $2,450.
i. Paid Bingham Company $970 to apply on account.
j. Paid $275 for continuing education course (Miscellaneous Expense).
k. Chin withdrew $2,200 for personal use.

Instructions

1. Record the transactions and the balances after each transaction, using the following headings:

Assets	= Liabilities +	Owner's Equity	
Cash + Accts. Rec. + Supp. + Equip.	Accounts Payable	J. Chin, Capital	+ Revenue − Expenses

2. Demonstrate that the total of one side of the equation equals the total of the other side of the equation.
3. Prepare an income statement and a statement of owner's equity for November and a balance sheet as of November 30.

SOLUTION

	Assets				= Liabilities +	Owner's Equity		
	Cash	+ Accts. Rec.	+ Supp.	+ Equip.	Accounts Payable	J. Chin, Capital	+ Revenue	− Expenses
(a)	+13,500					+13,500		
(b)	−1,600							+1,600 (Rent Expense)
Bal.	11,900 +	+	+	=	+	13,500 +	−	1,600
(c)	−6,700		+9,500		+2,800			
Bal.	5,200 +	+	+	9,500 =	2,800 +	13,500 +	−	1,600
(d)			+970		+970			
Bal.	5,200 +	+	970 +	9,500 =	3,770 +	13,500 +	−	1,600
(e)		+5,500					+5,500 (Client Fees)	
Bal.	5,200 +	5,500 +	970 +	9,500 =	3,770 +	13,500 +	5,500 −	1,600
(f)	−1,450							+1,450 (Salary Expense)
Bal.	3,750 +	5,500 +	970 +	9,500 =	3,770 +	13,500 +	5,500 −	3,050
(g)	−210							+210 (Telephone Expense)
Bal.	3,540 +	5,500 +	970 +	9,500 =	3,770 +	13,500 +	5,500 −	3,260
(h)	+2,450	−2,450						
Bal.	5,990 +	3,050 +	970 +	9,500 =	3,770 +	13,500 +	5,500 −	3,260
(i)	−970				−970			
Bal.	5,020 +	3,050 +	970 +	9,500 =	2,800 +	13,500 +	5,500 −	3,260
(j)	−275							+275 (Miscellaneous Expense)
Bal.	4,745 +	3,050 +	970 +	9,500 =	2,800 +	13,500 +	5,500 −	3,535
(k)	−2,200					−2,200 (Drawing)		
Bal.	2,545 +	3,050 +	970 +	9,500 =	2,800 +	11,300 +	5,500 −	3,535

James Chin, C.P.A.
Income Statement
For Month Ended November 30, 19—

Revenue:		
Client Fees		$5 5 0 0 00
Expenses:		
Rent Expense	$1 6 0 0 00	
Salary Expense	1 4 5 0 00	
Telephone Expense	2 1 0 00	
Miscellaneous Expense	2 7 5 00	
Total Expenses		3 5 3 5 00
Net Income		$1 9 6 5 00

SOLUTION (continued)

James Chin, C.P.A.
Statement of Owner's Equity
For Month Ended November 30, 19—

J. Chin, Capital, November 1, 19—							$13	5	0	0	00	
Net Income for November	$1	9	6	5	00							
Less Withdrawals for November	2	2	0	0	00							
Decrease in Capital								2	3	5	00	
J. Chin, Capital, November 30, 19—							$13	2	6	5	00	

James Chin, C.P.A.
Balance Sheet
November 30, 19—

Assets												
Cash	$2	5	4	5	00							
Accounts Receivable	3	0	5	0	00							
Supplies		9	7	0	00							
Equipment	9	5	0	0	00							
Total Assets							$16	0	6	5	00	
Liabilities												
Accounts Payable							$ 2	8	0	0	00	
Owner's Equity												
J. Chin, Capital							13	2	6	5	00	
Total Liabilities and Owner's Equity							$16	0	6	5	00	

PROBLEM 2-1A or 2-1B

	Assets				=	Liabilities	+	Owner's Equity		
	Cash	+	Supplies	+		Accounts Payable	+	Capital	, + Revenue	− Expenses
(a)				+			+		+	−
(b)										
Bal.	+		+	+	=		+		+	−
(c)										
Bal.	+		+	+	=		+		+	−
(d)										
Bal.	+		+	+	=		+		+	−
(e)										
Bal.	+		+	+	=		+		+	−
(f)										
Bal.	+		+	+	=		+		+	−
(g)										
Bal.	+		+	+	=		+		+	−
(h)										
Bal.	+		+	+	=		+		+	−
(i)										
Bal.	+		+	+	=		+		+	−
(j)										
Bal.	+		+	+	=		+		+	−
(k)										
Bal.	+		+	+	=		+		+	−

PROBLEM 2-1A or 2-1B (continued)

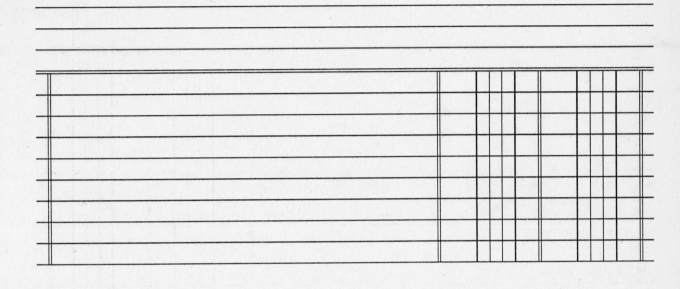

PROBLEM 2-1A or 2-1B (concluded)

PROBLEM 2-2A or 2-2B

	Assets				=	Liabilities	+	Owner's Equity		
	Cash	+ Supplies	+ Prepaid Insurance	+	=	Accounts Payable	+	Capital	+ Revenue	− Expenses
(a)										
(b)										
Bal.										
(c)										
Bal.										
(d)										
Bal.										
(e)										
Bal.										
(f)										
Bal.										
(g)										
Bal.										
(h)										
Bal.										
(i)										
Bal.										
(j)										
Bal.										
(k)										
Bal.										
(l)										
Bal.										
(m)										
Bal.										

PROBLEM 2-2A or 2-2B (continued)

PROBLEM 2-2A or 2-2B (concluded)

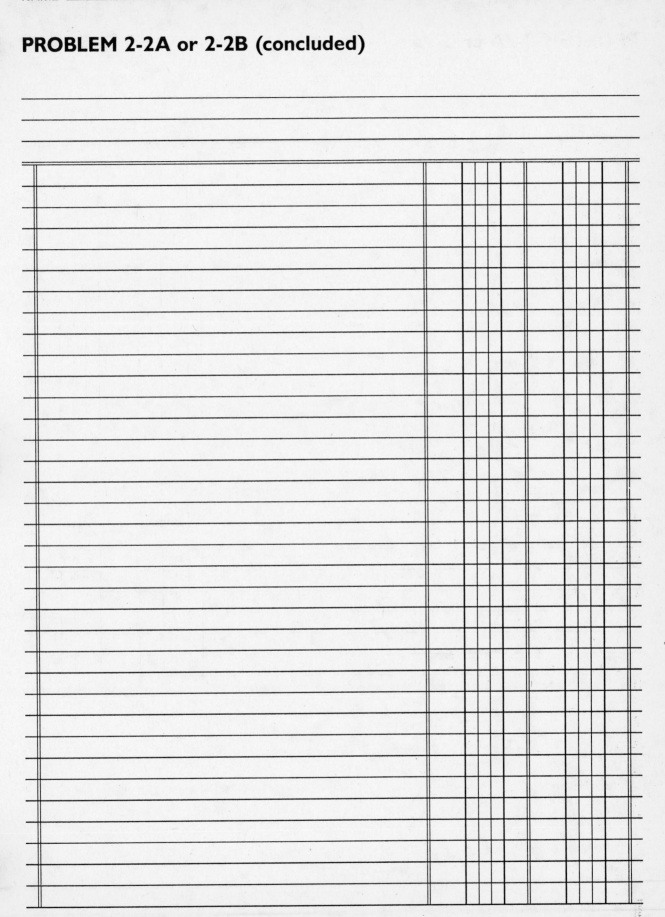

PROBLEM 2-3A or 2-3B

PROBLEM 2-3A or 2-3B (concluded)

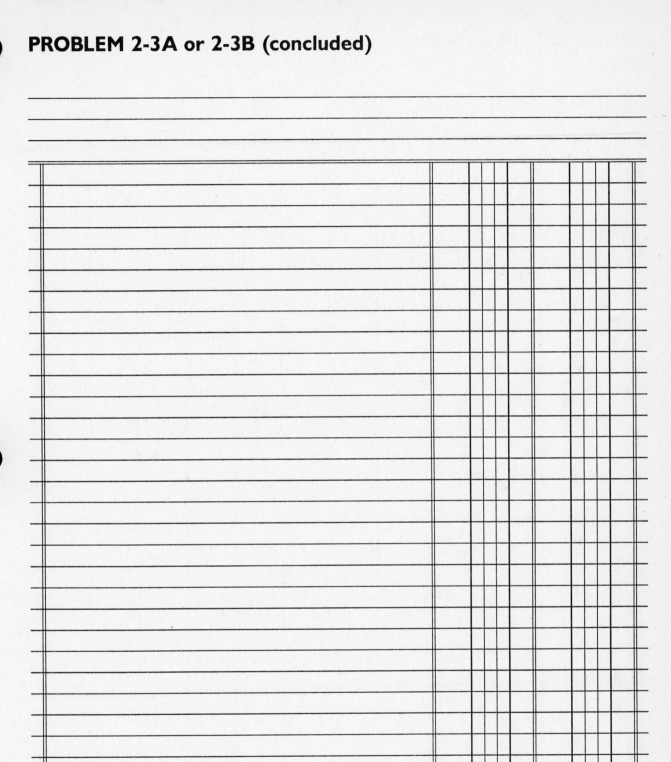

PROBLEM 2-4A or 2-4B

	Assets				=	Liabilities	+	Owner's Equity		
	Cash	+ Accounts Receivable	+ Supplies	+ Prepaid Insurance	+	=	Accounts Payable	+	Capital	, + Revenue	− Expenses
(a)											
(b)										+	−
Bal.	+	+	+	+	=	+	+	+	−
(c)										+	−
Bal.	+	+	+	+	=	+	+	+	−
(d)										+	−
Bal.	+	+	+	+	=	+	+	+	−
(e)										+	−
Bal.	+	+	+	+	=	+	+	+	−
(f)										+	−
Bal.	+	+	+	+	=	+	+	+	−
(g)										+	−
Bal.	+	+	+	+	=	+	+	+	−
(h)										+	−
Bal.	+	+	+	+	=	+	+	+	−
(i)										+	−
Bal.	+	+	+	+	=	+	+	+	−
(j)										+	−
Bal.	+	+	+	+	=	+	+	+	−
(k)										+	−
Bal.	+	+	+	+	=	+	+	+	−
(l)										+	−
Bal.	+	+	+	+	=	+	+	+	−
(m)										+	−
Bal.	+	+	+	+	=	+	+	+	−

PROBLEM 2-4A or 2-4B (continued)

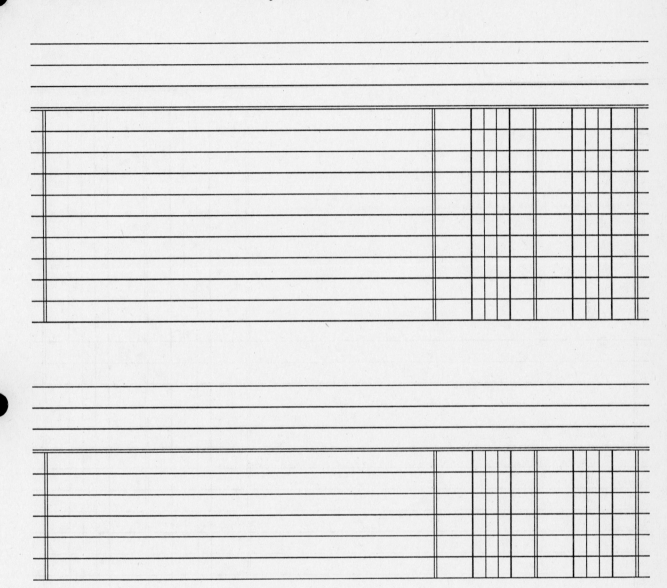

PROBLEM 2-4A or 2-4B (concluded)

Recording Business Transactions in T Account Form; The Trial Balance

LEARNING OBJECTIVES

1. Determine balances of T accounts having entries recorded on both sides of the accounts.
2. Present the fundamental accounting equation with the T account form, and label the plus and minus sides.
3. Record directly in T accounts a group of business transactions involving changes in asset, liability, owner's equity, revenue, and expense accounts for a service business.
4. Present the fundamental accounting equation with the T account form, and label the debit and credit sides.
5. Prepare a trial balance.
6. Recognize the effect of transpositions and slides on account balances.

KEY TERMS

Compound entry
Credit
Debit
Footings
Normal balance

Separate entity concept
Slide
T account form
Transposition
Trial balance

STUDY GUIDE QUESTIONS

PART 1   True/False

For each of the following statements, circle T if the statement is true and F if the statement is false.

T   F   1. Increases in assets are recorded on the credit side.

T   F   2. The normal balance of an expense account is on the debit side.

T   F   3. When debits total $4,100 and credits total $5,200, the balance in the T account is recorded on the credit side.

T   F   4. Decreases in liabilities are recorded on the credit side.

T   F   5. In a trial balance, the balance of the Prepaid Insurance account appears in the credit column.

T   F   6. Recording $41.60 as $4.16 is an example of a transposition.

T   F   7. In a single transaction, it is possible to have more than one credit.

T   F   8. In a trial balance, the balance of Accounts Receivable appears on the credit side.

T   F   9. The T form of an account makes it possible to record increases on one side of the account and decreases on the other side of the account.

T   F   10. The credit side is the right-hand side of any T account.

PART 2   Completion—Language of Business

Complete each of the following statements by writing the appropriate word(s) in the spaces provided.

1. The left-hand side of any account is the _____ side.
2. The small, pencilled-in figures used to record the totals of each side of a T account are called _____ .
3. In the recording of a number, if the digits are switched around, the error is called a(n) _____ .
4. The device used to prove that the total of all the debit balances equals the total of all the credit balances is called a(n) _____ .
5. A(n) _____ is used to record a transaction that has more than one debit and/or more than one credit.
6. The right-hand side of any account is called the _____ side.

PART 3   Accounting Entries

The following transactions were completed by C. R. Hendriks, Physical Therapist. Using appropriate account titles, record the transactions in pairs of T accounts, and show plus and minus signs with each T account. List accounts to be debited in the left-hand T account column and accounts to be credited in the right-hand T account column.

		Utilities Expense			Cash	
		+	−		+	−
0.	*Example:* Paid electric bill, $92.	(0) 92				(0) 92
a.	Bought professional equipment on account, $760.					
b.	Billed patients for services performed, $764.					
c.	Paid rent for the month, $950.					
d.	Bought supplies on account, $410.					
e.	Paid telephone bill, $76.					
f.	Collected $610 from patients previously billed.					
g.	Paid creditors on account, $500.					

h. Paid salary of assistant, $990.

i. Bought office equipment for cash, $342.

j. Returned $200 of supplies bought previously on credit in **d** and received a reduction in the bill.

DEMONSTRATION PROBLEM

Dr. Christy Russo maintains an office for the practice of veterinary medicine. The account balances as of August 1 are given below. All are normal balances.

Assets		Revenue	
Cash	$ 2,459	Professional Fees	$72,118
Accounts Receivable	18,120	**Expenses**	
Supplies	840	Salary Expense	14,380
Prepaid Insurance	980	Rent Expense	10,320
Furniture and Equipment	5,963	Automobile Expense	859
Automobile	20,650	Utilities Expense	1,213
Liabilities			
Accounts Payable	1,590		
Owner's Equity			
C. Russo, Capital	42,076		
C. Russo, Drawing	40,000		

The following transactions occurred during August of this year:

a. Paid rent for the month, $1,290.
b. Paid $1,800 for liability insurance.
c. Bought medical equipment on account from Bennett Surgical Supply, $849, paying $200 down with the balance due in thirty days.
d. Billed patients for services performed, $9,015.
e. Paid employee salaries, $1,797.
f. Received and paid gas and electric bill, $112.
g. Received from patients previously billed, $11,060.
h. Received bill for gasoline for car, used only in the professional practice, from Garza Fuel company, $116.
i. Paid creditors on account, $1,590.
j. Dr. Russo withdrew cash for personal use, $5,000.

Instructions

1. Correctly place plus and minus signs under each T account and label the sides of the T accounts as either debit or credit in the fundamental accounting equation. Record the account balances as of August 1.
2. Record the August transactions in the T accounts. Key each transaction to the letter that identifies the transaction.
3. Foot the columns.
4. Prepare a trial balance with the correct three-line heading, dated August 31.

SOLUTION

Assets	=	Liabilities	+	Owner's Equity	+	Revenue	−	Expenses
+	−	−	+	−	+	−	+	+	−
Debit	Credit	Debit	Credit	Debit	Credit	Debit	Credit	Debit	Credit

Cash

+	−
Bal. 2,459	(a) 1,290
(g) 11,060	(b) 1,800
13,519	(c) 200
	(e) 1,797
	(f) 112
	(i) 1,590
	(j) 5,000
	11,789

Bal. 1,730

Accounts Receivable

+	−
Bal. 18,120	(g) 11,060
(d) 9,015	
27,135	

Bal. 16,075

Supplies

+	−
Bal. 840	

Prepaid Insurance

+	−
Bal. 980	
(b) 1,800	

Bal. 2,780

Furniture and Equipment

+	−
Bal. 5,963	
(c) 849	

Bal. 6,812

Automobile

+	−
Bal. 20,650	

Accounts Payable

−	+
(i) 1,590	Bal. 1,590
	(c) 649
	(h) 116
	2,355

Bal. 765

C. Russo, Capital

−	+
	Bal. 42,076

C. Russo, Drawing

+	−
Bal. 40,000	
(j) 5,000	

Bal. 45,000

Professional Fees

−	+
	Bal. 72,118
	(d) 9,015

Bal. 81,133

Salary Expense

+	−
Bal. 14,380	
(e) 1,797	

Bal. 16,177

Rent Expense

+	−
Bal. 10,320	
(a) 1,290	

Bal. 11,610

Automobile Expense

+	−
Bal. 859	
(h) 116	

Bal. 975

Utilities Expense

+	−
Bal. 1,213	
(f) 112	

Bal. 1,325

Dr. Christy Russo
Trial Balance
August 31, 19—

ACCOUNT NAME	DEBIT	CREDIT
Cash	1 7 3 0 00	
Accounts Receivable	16 0 7 5 00	
Supplies	8 4 0 00	
Prepaid Insurance	2 7 8 0 00	
Furniture and Equipment	6 8 1 2 00	
Automobile	20 6 5 0 00	
Accounts Payable		7 6 5 00
C. Russo, Capital		42 0 7 6 00
C. Russo, Drawing	45 0 0 0 00	
Professional Fees		81 1 3 3 00
Salary Expense	16 1 7 7 00	
Rent Expense	11 6 1 0 00	
Automobile Expense	9 7 5 00	
Utilities Expense	1 3 2 5 00	
	123 9 7 4 00	123 9 7 4 00

PROBLEM 3-1A or 3-1B

Expenses

−

Revenue

+

Owner's Equity

+

Liabilities

=

Assets

PROBLEM 3-2A or 3-2B

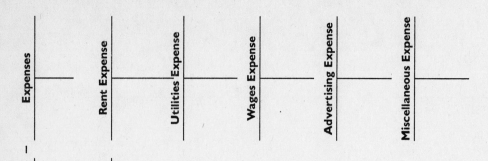

Expenses

| Rent Expense | Utilities Expense | Wages Expense | Advertising Expense | Miscellaneous Expense |

−

Revenue

Income from Services

+

Owner's Equity

Capital

Drawing

+

Liabilities

Accounts Payable

=

Assets

| Cash | Supplies | Computer Programs | Office Equipment | Neon Sign |

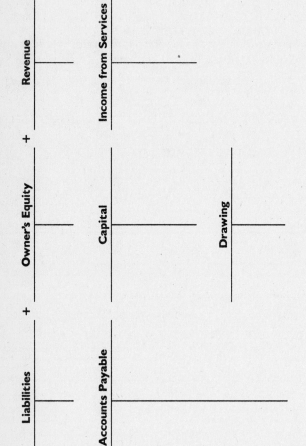

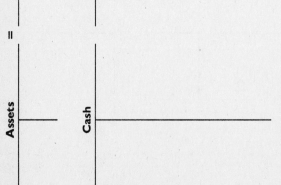

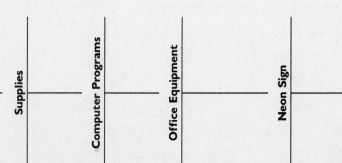

PROBLEM 3-2A or 3-2B (concluded)

ACCOUNT NAME	DEBIT	CREDIT

PROBLEM 3-3A or 3-3B

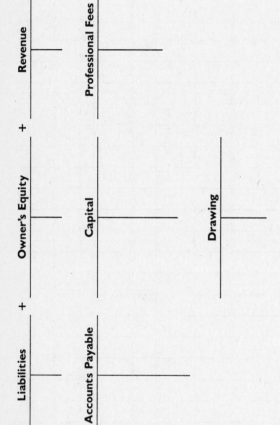
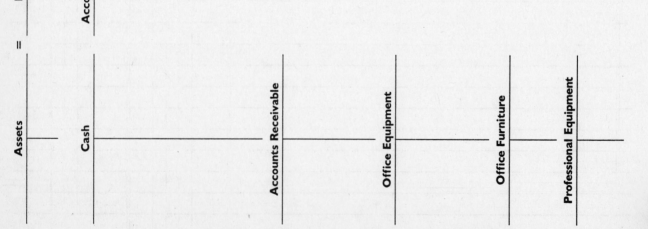
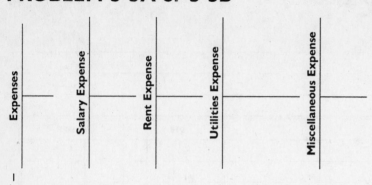

PROBLEM 3-3A or 3-3B (continued)

ACCOUNT NAME	DEBIT	CREDIT

PROBLEM 3-3A or 3-3B (continued)

PROBLEM 3-3A or 3-3B (concluded)

PROBLEM 3-4A or 3-4B

Cash

Accounts Payable

Utilities Expense

Miscellaneous Expense

, Capital

Supplies

, Drawing

Prepaid Insurance

Coin Box Revenue

Equipment

Wages Expense

Furniture and Fixtures

Rent Expense

PROBLEM 3-4A or 3-4B (continued)

ACCOUNT NAME	DEBIT	CREDIT

PROBLEM 3-4A or 3-4B (concluded)

4 The General Journal and the General Ledger

LEARNING OBJECTIVES

1. Record a group of transactions pertaining to a service-type enterprise in a two-column general journal.
2. Post entries from a two-column general journal to general ledger accounts.
3. Prepare a trial balance from the ledger accounts.
4. Correct entries using the ruling method.
5. Correct entries using the correcting entry method.

KEY TERMS

Account numbers
Chart of accounts
Cost principle
Cross-reference
General ledger
Journal

Journalizing
Ledger account
Posting
Source documents
Two-column general journal

STUDY GUIDE QUESTIONS

PART 1   True/False

For each of the following statements, circle T if the statement is true and F if the statement is false.

T   F   1. The credit part of a journal entry always comes first.

T   F   2. Dollar signs are required in all journal entries.

T   F   3. A transaction must be posted before it is journalized.

T   F   4. In a journal entry, if two accounts are debited, two accounts must be credited.

T   F   5. The first step in the posting process is to write the date of the transaction.

T   F   6. In the presentation of a general journal in the text, the title of the account credited is indented approximately one-half inch.

T   F   7. A number in the Posting Reference column in the ledger account indicates that the balance has been recorded in the trial balance.

T   F   8. Failure to post an entire transaction from the journal to the ledger will show up in the trial balance.

T   F   9. Having a running balance is an advantage of a four-column ledger account form.

T   F   10. A trial balance is prepared directly from the journal.

PART 2 Completion—Language of Business

Complete each of the following statements by writing the appropriate words in the spaces provided.

1. The list of account titles and account numbers to be used for a specific business is called a(n) _____ .

2. The process of transferring information from the journal to the ledger is called _____ _____ .

3. Business papers that serve as evidence that a transaction took place are called _____ _____ .

4. The _____ states that the purchase of an asset should be recorded at the agreed amount of the transaction.

5. The process of recording a business transaction in a book of original entry is called ____ _____ .

6. A cross-reference exists when the journal page number is recorded in the Posting Reference column of the ledger and the ledger account number is recorded in the _____ _____ .

7. The accounts in the ledger are listed according to _____ .

PART 3 Completing a Journal Entry

Here are a partially completed journal entry and the Cash ledger account. Complete the entry, including the explanation, using the following data. The name of the charge customer is M. L. Bates Company. The entry represents the first entry on page 33 and occurred during October of the current year.

GENERAL JOURNAL

PAGE _____

	DATE		DESCRIPTION	POST. REF.	DEBIT	CREDIT	
1	19—						1
2	Oct.	29	Cash		1 1 0 0 00		2
3			Accounts Receivable	113			3
4			Income from Services	411		1 7 0 0 00	4
5							5
6							6
7							7
8							8

GENERAL LEDGER

ACCOUNT Cash   ACCOUNT NO. 111

DATE		ITEM	POST. REF.	DEBIT	CREDIT	BALANCE DEBIT	BALANCE CREDIT
19—							
Oct.	6		30	6 0 0 00		3 5 0 0 00	
	6		30		7 0 0 00	2 8 0 0 00	
	12		32	1 1 0 0 00		3 9 0 0 00	
	14		32		4 0 0 00	3 5 0 0 00	
	27		32		2 0 0 00	3 3 0 0 00	
	29		33	1 1 0 0 00		4 4 0 0 00	

1. What is the missing amount in the journal entry? _____
2. What is the total cash received during October? _____
3. What is the total cash paid out during October? _____
4. The journal entry is an example of a(n) _____ journal entry.

DEMONSTRATION PROBLEM

D. L. DeDonato, a fitness enthusiast, buys an existing exercise studio, Body Firm, with the following chart of accounts:

Assets
111 Cash
112 Supplies
121 Equipment
123 Building
125 Land

Liabilities
211 Accounts Payable
213 Mortgage Payable

Owner's Equity
311 D. L. DeDonato, Capital
312 D. L. DeDonato, Drawing

Revenue
411 Income from Services

Expenses
511 Wages Expense
512 Utilities Expense
513 Advertising Expense
514 Repair Expense
519 Miscellaneous Expense

Apr. 16 DeDonato deposited $100,000 in a bank account for the purpose of buying Body Firm.

17 Bought the assets of Body Firm for a total price of $178,000. The assets include supplies, $750; equipment, $17,250; building, $96,000; and land, $64,000. Made a down payment of $89,000 and signed a mortgage note for the remainder.

17 Bought additional equipment from Fitness Supply Co. on account for $3,550, paying $710 down, with balance due in 30 days.

29 Celebrated the grand opening of Body Firm. Advertising expenses were paid in cash for the following:

Advertising in newspaper	$314
Announcements mailed to local residences	85
Postage	125
Balloons, ribbons, flowers	126
Food and refreshments	58

30 Received fees for daily use of the facilities, $752.

30 Paid wages for the period April 17 through April 30, $833.

30 Received and paid electric bill, $129.

30 Received and paid repair bill, $96.

30 DeDonato withdrew $600 for personal use.

Instructions

Record the transactions in general journal form.

SOLUTION

GENERAL JOURNAL

DATE		DESCRIPTION	POST. REF.	DEBIT	CREDIT
19—					
Apr.	16	Cash		100 0 0 0 00	
		D. L. DeDonato, Capital			100 0 0 0 00
		Invested cash in the business.			
	17	Supplies		7 5 0 00	
		Equipment		17 2 5 0 00	
		Building		96 0 0 0 00	
		Land		64 0 0 0 00	
		Cash			89 0 0 0 00
		Mortgage Payable			89 0 0 0 00
		Bought Body Firm.			
	17	Equipment		3 5 5 0 00	
		Cash			7 1 0 00
		Accounts Payable			2 8 4 0 00
		Bought equipment on account from			
		Fitness Supply Co., with balance			
		due in 30 days.			
	29	Advertising Expense		7 0 8 00	
		Cash			7 0 8 00
		Grand opening expenses.			
	30	Cash		7 5 2 00	
		Income from Services			7 5 2 00
		Received fees.			
	30	Wages Expense		8 3 3 00	
		Cash			8 3 3 00
		Paid wages for period April 17			
		through April 30.			
	30	Utilities Expense		1 2 9 00	
		Cash			1 2 9 00
		Paid electric bill.			

SOLUTION (concluded)

GENERAL JOURNAL

DATE		DESCRIPTION	POST. REF.	DEBIT	CREDIT
19—					
Apr.	30	Repair Expense		9 6 00	
		Cash			9 6 00
		Paid repair bill.			
	30	D. L. DeDonato, Drawing		6 0 0 00	
		Cash			6 0 0 00
		Withdrawal for personal use.			

PROBLEM 4-1A or 4-1B

GENERAL JOURNAL

PAGE _____

	DATE	DESCRIPTION	POST. REF.	DEBIT	CREDIT	
1						1
2						2
3						3
4						4
5						5
6						6
7						7
8						8
9						9
10						10
11						11
12						12
13						13
14						14
15						15
16						16
17						17
18						18
19						19
20						20
21						21
22						22
23						23
24						24
25						25
26						26
27						27
28						28
29						29
30						30
31						31
32						32
33						33
34						34
35						35
36						36
37						37

PROBLEM 4-1A or 4-1B (continued)

GENERAL JOURNAL

	DATE	DESCRIPTION	POST. REF.	DEBIT	CREDIT	
1						1
2						2
3						3
4						4
5						5
6						6
7						7
8						8
9						9
10						10
11						11
12						12
13						13
14						14
15						15
16						16
17						17
18						18
19						19
20						20
21						21
22						22
23						23
24						24
25						25
26						26
27						27
28						28
29						29
30						30
31						31
32						32
33						33
34						34
35						35
36						36
37						37

PROBLEM 4-1A or 4-1B (concluded)

GENERAL JOURNAL

PAGE _____

	DATE		DESCRIPTION	POST. REF.	DEBIT	CREDIT	
1							1
2							2
3							3
4							4
5							5
6							6
7							7
8							8
9							9
10							10
11							11
12							12
13							13
14							14
15							15
16							16
17							17
18							18
19							19
20							20
21							21
22							22
23							23
24							24
25							25
26							26
27							27
28							28
29							29
30							30
31							31
32							32
33							33
34							34
35							35
36							36
37							37

PROBLEM 4-2A

GENERAL JOURNAL

PAGE ____4____

	DATE		DESCRIPTION	POST. REF.	DEBIT	CREDIT	
1	19—						1
2	July	1	Rent Expense		5 0 0 00		2
3			Cash			5 0 0 00	3
4			Paid rent for July.				4
5							5
6		3	Cash		5 0 00		6
7			Accounts Receivable			5 0 00	7
8			Formal Rentals apply on account.				8
9							9
10		7	Cash		1 8 6 4 00		10
11			Income from Services			1 8 6 4 00	11
12			For week ended July 7.				12
13							13
14		9	Accounts Payable		2 4 0 00		14
15			Cash			2 4 0 00	15
16			Paid Drake Equipment Company				16
17			on account.				17
18							18
19		14	Cash		1 6 0 8 00		19
20			Income from Services			1 6 0 8 00	20
21			For week ended July 14.				21
22							22
23		15	Wages Expense		6 4 4 00		23
24			Cash			6 4 4 00	24
25			Paid wages, June 25–July 15.				25
26							26
27		17	Accounts Receivable		2 8 0 00		27
28			Income from Services			2 8 0 00	28
29			Formal Rentals, for services				29
30			rendered.				30
31							31
32		19	Supplies		5 8 0 00		32
33			Accounts Payable			5 8 0 00	33
34			Bought supplies on account from				34
35			Blair and Company.				35
36							36
37							37

PROBLEM 4-2A (continued)

GENERAL JOURNAL PAGE ____ 5

	DATE		DESCRIPTION	POST. REF.	DEBIT	CREDIT	
1	19—						1
2	July	21	Cash		1 6 8 0 00		2
3			Income from Services			1 6 8 0 00	3
4			For week ended July 21.				4
5							5
6		25	Utilities Expense		5 0 4 00		6
7			Cash			5 0 4 00	7
8			Paid electric bill.				8
9							9
10		26	Accounts Payable		2 0 0 00		10
11			Cash			2 0 0 00	11
12			Paid Blair and Company on				12
13			account.				13
14							14
15		29	Wages Expense		5 9 6 00		15
16			Cash			5 9 6 00	16
17			Paid wages, July 16–July 29.				17
18							18
19		31	Cash		8 3 0 00		19
20			Income from Services			8 3 0 00	20
21			For remainder of July.				21
22							22
23		31	Cash		1 0 0 00		23
24			Accounts Receivable			1 0 0 00	24
25			Formal Rentals, to apply on				25
26			account.				26
27							27
28		31	Advertising Expense		1 6 4 00		28
29			Accounts Payable			1 6 4 00	29
30			Received advertising bill from				30
31			City News.				31
32							32
33		31	N. L. Clark, Drawing		1 4 0 0 00		33
34			Cash			1 4 0 0 00	34
35			Withdrawal for personal use.				35
36							36
37							37

PROBLEM 4-2A (continued)

GENERAL LEDGER

ACCOUNT _Cash_   ACCOUNT NO. _111_

DATE		ITEM	POST. REF.	DEBIT	CREDIT	BALANCE DEBIT	BALANCE CREDIT
19—							
July	1	Balance	✓			15 4 9 0 00	

ACCOUNT _Accounts Receivable_   ACCOUNT NO. _112_

DATE		ITEM	POST. REF.	DEBIT	CREDIT	BALANCE DEBIT	BALANCE CREDIT
19—							
July	1	Balance	✓			5 0 00	

ACCOUNT _Supplies_   ACCOUNT NO. _113_

DATE		ITEM	POST. REF.	DEBIT	CREDIT	BALANCE DEBIT	BALANCE CREDIT
19—							
July	1	Balance	✓			4 0 0 00	

PROBLEM 4-2A (continued)

ACCOUNT _Prepaid Insurance_ ACCOUNT NO. _114_

DATE		ITEM	POST. REF.	DEBIT	CREDIT	BALANCE	
						DEBIT	CREDIT
19—							
July	1	Balance	✓			3 6 0 00	

ACCOUNT _Equipment_ ACCOUNT NO. _121_

DATE		ITEM	POST. REF.	DEBIT	CREDIT	BALANCE	
						DEBIT	CREDIT
19—							
July	1	Balance	✓			26 9 4 0 00	

ACCOUNT _Accounts Payable_ ACCOUNT NO. _211_

DATE		ITEM	POST. REF.	DEBIT	CREDIT	BALANCE	
						DEBIT	CREDIT
19—							
July	1	Balance	✓				2 4 0 0 00

ACCOUNT _N. L. Clark, Capital_ ACCOUNT NO. _311_

DATE		ITEM	POST. REF.	DEBIT	CREDIT	BALANCE	
						DEBIT	CREDIT
19—							
July	1	Balance	✓				40 0 0 0 00

PROBLEM 4-2A (continued)

ACCOUNT *N. L. Clark, Drawing*   ACCOUNT NO. *312*

DATE	ITEM	POST. REF.	DEBIT	CREDIT	BALANCE DEBIT	BALANCE CREDIT
19—						
July 1	Balance	✓			1 2 0 0 00	

ACCOUNT *Income from Services*   ACCOUNT NO. *411*

DATE	ITEM	POST. REF.	DEBIT	CREDIT	BALANCE DEBIT	BALANCE CREDIT
19—						
July 1	Balance	✓				3 8 7 0 00

ACCOUNT *Wages Expense*   ACCOUNT NO. *511*

DATE	ITEM	POST. REF.	DEBIT	CREDIT	BALANCE DEBIT	BALANCE CREDIT
19—						
July 1	Balance	✓			9 3 0 00	

ACCOUNT *Rent Expense*   ACCOUNT NO. *512*

DATE	ITEM	POST. REF.	DEBIT	CREDIT	BALANCE DEBIT	BALANCE CREDIT
19—						
July 1	Balance	✓			5 0 0 00	

PROBLEM 4-2A (continued)

ACCOUNT *Advertising Expense*   ACCOUNT NO. *513*

DATE		ITEM	POST. REF.	DEBIT	CREDIT	BALANCE	
						DEBIT	CREDIT
19—							
July	1	Balance	√			1 8 0 00	

ACCOUNT *Utilities Expense*   ACCOUNT NO. *514*

DATE		ITEM	POST. REF.	DEBIT	CREDIT	BALANCE	
						DEBIT	CREDIT
19—							
July	1	Balance	√			2 2 0 00	

ACCOUNT NAME	DEBIT	CREDIT

PROBLEM 4-2A (continued)

PROBLEM 4-2A (concluded)

PROBLEM 4-2B

GENERAL JOURNAL   PAGE ___4___

	DATE		DESCRIPTION	POST. REF.	DEBIT	CREDIT	
1	19—						1
2	July	1	Rent Expense		5 0 0 00		2
3			Cash			5 0 0 00	3
4			Paid rent for July.				4
5							5
6		3	Cash		3 0 00		6
7			Accounts Receivable			3 0 00	7
8			Formal Rentals apply on				8
9			account.				9
10							10
11		7	Cash		1 9 4 4 00		11
12			Income from Services			1 9 4 4 00	12
13			For week ended July 7.				13
14							14
15		9	Accounts Payable		2 7 0 00		15
16			Cash			2 7 0 00	16
17			Paid Drake Equipment Company				17
18			on account.				18
19							19
20		14	Cash		1 5 3 8 00		20
21			Income from Services			1 5 3 8 00	21
22			For week ended July 14.				22
23							23
24		15	Wages Expense		6 9 4 00		24
25			Cash			6 9 4 00	25
26			Paid wages, June 25–July 15.				26
27							27
28		17	Accounts Receivable		3 1 0 00		28
29			Income from Services			3 1 0 00	29
30			Rincon Motel, for services				30
31			rendered.				31
32							32
33		19	Supplies		6 2 0 00		33
34			Accounts Payable			6 2 0 00	34
35			Bought supplies on account				35
36			from Bates and Company.				36
37							37

PROBLEM 4-2B (continued)

GENERAL JOURNAL

PAGE _____ 5

	DATE		DESCRIPTION	POST. REF.	DEBIT	CREDIT	
1	19—						1
2	July	21	Cash		1 6 1 0 00		2
3			Income from Services			1 6 1 0 00	3
4			For week ended July 21.				4
5							5
6		25	Utilities Expense		4 9 4 00		6
7			Cash			4 9 4 00	7
8			Paid electric bill.				8
9							9
10		26	Accounts Payable		1 8 0 00		10
11			Cash			1 8 0 00	11
12			Paid Bates and Company on				12
13			account.				13
14							14
15		29	Wages Expense		6 1 6 00		15
16			Cash			6 1 6 00	16
17			Paid wages, July 16–July 29.				17
18							18
19		31	Cash		9 2 0 00		19
20			Income from Services			9 2 0 00	20
21			For remainder of July.				21
22							22
23		31	Cash		1 2 0 00		23
24			Accounts Receivable			1 2 0 00	24
25			Rincon Motel, to apply on				25
26			account.				26
27							27
28		31	Advertising Expense		1 7 4 00		28
29			Accounts Payable			1 7 4 00	29
30			Received advertising bill from				30
31			City News.				31
32							32
33		31	S. T. Hale, Drawing		1 9 2 0 00		33
34			Cash			1 9 2 0 00	34
35			Withdrawal for personal use.				35
36							36
37							37

PROBLEM 4-2B (continued)

GENERAL LEDGER

ACCOUNT _Cash_   ACCOUNT NO. _111_

DATE		ITEM	POST. REF.	DEBIT	CREDIT	BALANCE	
						DEBIT	CREDIT
19—							
July	1	Balance	✓			15 4 9 0 00	

ACCOUNT _Accounts Receivable_   ACCOUNT NO. _112_

DATE		ITEM	POST. REF.	DEBIT	CREDIT	BALANCE	
						DEBIT	CREDIT
19—							
July	1	Balance	✓			5 0 00	

ACCOUNT _Supplies_   ACCOUNT NO. _113_

DATE		ITEM	POST. REF.	DEBIT	CREDIT	BALANCE	
						DEBIT	CREDIT
19—							
July	1	Balance	✓			4 0 0 00	

PROBLEM 4-2B (continued)

ACCOUNT _Prepaid Insurance_   ACCOUNT NO. _114_

DATE		ITEM	POST. REF.	DEBIT	CREDIT	BALANCE DEBIT	BALANCE CREDIT
19—							
July	1	Balance	✓			3 6 0 00	

ACCOUNT _Equipment_   ACCOUNT NO. _121_

DATE		ITEM	POST. REF.	DEBIT	CREDIT	BALANCE DEBIT	BALANCE CREDIT
19—							
July	1	Balance	✓			26 9 4 0 00	

ACCOUNT _Accounts Payable_   ACCOUNT NO. _211_

DATE		ITEM	POST. REF.	DEBIT	CREDIT	BALANCE DEBIT	BALANCE CREDIT
19—							
July	1	Balance	✓				2 4 0 0 00

ACCOUNT _S.T. Hale, Capital_   ACCOUNT NO. _311_

DATE		ITEM	POST. REF.	DEBIT	CREDIT	BALANCE DEBIT	BALANCE CREDIT
19—							
July	1	Balance	✓				40 0 0 0 00

PROBLEM 4-2B (continued)

ACCOUNT __S. T. Hale, Drawing_____ ACCOUNT NO. __312__

DATE		ITEM	POST. REF.	DEBIT	CREDIT	BALANCE	
						DEBIT	CREDIT
19—							
July	1	Balance	√			1 2 0 0 00	

ACCOUNT __Income from Services_____ ACCOUNT NO. __411__

DATE		ITEM	POST. REF.	DEBIT	CREDIT	BALANCE	
						DEBIT	CREDIT
19—							
July	1	Balance	√				3 8 7 0 00

ACCOUNT __Wages Expense_____ ACCOUNT NO. __511__

DATE		ITEM	POST. REF.	DEBIT	CREDIT	BALANCE	
						DEBIT	CREDIT
19—							
July	1	Balance	√			9 3 0 00	

ACCOUNT __Rent Expense_____ ACCOUNT NO. __512__

DATE		ITEM	POST. REF.	DEBIT	CREDIT	BALANCE	
						DEBIT	CREDIT
19—							
July	1	Balance	√			5 0 0 00	

PROBLEM 4-2B (continued)

ACCOUNT *Advertising Expense*   ACCOUNT NO. *513*

DATE		ITEM	POST. REF.	DEBIT	CREDIT	BALANCE	
						DEBIT	CREDIT
19—							
July	*1*	*Balance*	✓			*1 8 0 00*	

ACCOUNT *Utilities Expense*   ACCOUNT NO. *514*

DATE		ITEM	POST. REF.	DEBIT	CREDIT	BALANCE	
						DEBIT	CREDIT
19—							
July	*1*	*Balance*	✓			*2 2 0 00*	

ACCOUNT NAME	DEBIT	CREDIT

PROBLEM 4-2B (continued)

PROBLEM 4-2B (concluded)

PROBLEM 4-3A or 4-3B

GENERAL JOURNAL

PAGE _____

	DATE		DESCRIPTION	POST. REF.	DEBIT	CREDIT	
1							1
2							2
3							3
4							4
5							5
6							6
7							7
8							8
9							9
10							10
11							11
12							12
13							13
14							14
15							15
16							16
17							17
18							18
19							19
20							20
21							21
22							22
23							23
24							24
25							25
26							26
27							27
28							28
29							29
30							30
31							31
32							32
33							33
34							34
35							35
36							36
37							37

PROBLEM 4-3A or 4-3B (continued)

GENERAL JOURNAL

	DATE		DESCRIPTION	POST. REF.	DEBIT	CREDIT	
1							1
2							2
3							3
4							4
5							5
6							6
7							7
8							8
9							9
10							10
11							11
12							12
13							13
14							14
15							15
16							16
17							17
18							18
19							19
20							20
21							21
22							22
23							23
24							24
25							25
26							26
27							27
28							28
29							29
30							30
31							31
32							32
33							33
34							34
35							35
36							36
37							37

PROBLEM 4-3A or 4-3B (continued)

GENERAL LEDGER

ACCOUNT *Cash* _____ ACCOUNT NO. *111*

DATE	ITEM	POST. REF.	DEBIT	CREDIT	BALANCE DEBIT	BALANCE CREDIT
19—						
Feb. 1	Balance	✓			2 8 9 0 00	

ACCOUNT *Accounts Receivable* _____ ACCOUNT NO. *112*

DATE	ITEM	POST. REF.	DEBIT	CREDIT	BALANCE DEBIT	BALANCE CREDIT
19—						
Feb. 1	Balance	✓			3 2 4 0 00	

ACCOUNT *Supplies* _____ ACCOUNT NO. *113*

DATE	ITEM	POST. REF.	DEBIT	CREDIT	BALANCE DEBIT	BALANCE CREDIT
19—						
Feb. 1	Balance	✓			1 5 2 00	

ACCOUNT *Prepaid Insurance* _____ ACCOUNT NO. *114*

DATE	ITEM	POST. REF.	DEBIT	CREDIT	BALANCE DEBIT	BALANCE CREDIT
19—						
Feb. 1	Balance	✓			2 2 8 0 00	

PROBLEM 4-3A or 4-3B (continued)

ACCOUNT **Equipment** ACCOUNT NO. _**121**_

DATE		ITEM	POST. REF.	DEBIT	CREDIT	BALANCE	
						DEBIT	CREDIT
19—							
Feb.	1	Balance	√			11 9 0 0 00	

ACCOUNT **Accounts Payable** ACCOUNT NO. _**211**_

DATE		ITEM	POST. REF.	DEBIT	CREDIT	BALANCE	
						DEBIT	CREDIT
19—							
Feb.	1	Balance	√				1 7 3 2 00

ACCOUNT **B. L. Hintzen, Capital** ACCOUNT NO. _**311**_

DATE		ITEM	POST. REF.	DEBIT	CREDIT	BALANCE	
						DEBIT	CREDIT
19—							
Feb.	1	Balance	√				18 7 3 0 00

ACCOUNT **B. L. Hintzen, Drawing** ACCOUNT NO. _**312**_

DATE		ITEM	POST. REF.	DEBIT	CREDIT	BALANCE	
						DEBIT	CREDIT

ACCOUNT **Professional Fees** ACCOUNT NO. _**411**_

DATE		ITEM	POST. REF.	DEBIT	CREDIT	BALANCE	
						DEBIT	CREDIT

PROBLEM 4-3A or 4-3B (continued)

ACCOUNT _Salary Expense_ _____ ACCOUNT NO. _511_

DATE	ITEM	POST. REF.	DEBIT	CREDIT	BALANCE	
					DEBIT	CREDIT

ACCOUNT _Advertising Expense_ _____ ACCOUNT NO. _512_

DATE	ITEM	POST. REF.	DEBIT	CREDIT	BALANCE	
					DEBIT	CREDIT

ACCOUNT _Rent Expense_ _____ ACCOUNT NO. _513_

DATE	ITEM	POST. REF.	DEBIT	CREDIT	BALANCE	
					DEBIT	CREDIT

ACCOUNT _Utilities Expense_ _____ ACCOUNT NO. _514_

DATE	ITEM	POST. REF.	DEBIT	CREDIT	BALANCE	
					DEBIT	CREDIT

PROBLEM 4-3A or 4-3B (concluded)

ACCOUNT NAME	DEBIT	CREDIT

PROBLEM 4-4A or 4-4B

GENERAL JOURNAL

	DATE	DESCRIPTION	POST. REF.	DEBIT	CREDIT	
1						1
2						2
3						3
4						4
5						5
6						6
7						7
8						8
9						9
10						10
11						11
12						12
13						13
14						14
15						15
16						16
17						17
18						18
19						19
20						20
21						21
22						22
23						23
24						24
25						25
26						26
27						27
28						28
29						29
30						30
31						31
32						32
33						33
34						34
35						35
36						36
37						37

PROBLEM 4-4A or 4-4B (continued)

GENERAL JOURNAL   PAGE _____

	DATE	DESCRIPTION	POST. REF.	DEBIT	CREDIT	
1						1
2						2
3						3
4						4
5						5
6						6
7						7
8						8
9						9
10						10
11						11
12						12
13						13
14						14
15						15
16						16
17						17
18						18
19						19
20						20
21						21
22						22
23						23
24						24
25						25
26						26
27						27
28						28
29						29
30						30
31						31
32						32
33						33
34						34
35						35
36						36
37						37

PROBLEM 4-4A or 4-4B (continued)

GENERAL JOURNAL   PAGE _____

	DATE	DESCRIPTION	POST. REF.	DEBIT	CREDIT	
1						1
2						2
3						3
4						4
5						5
6						6
7						7
8						8
9						9
10						10
11						11
12						12
13						13
14						14
15						15
16						16
17						17
18						18
19						19
20						20
21						21
22						22
23						23
24						24
25						25
26						26
27						27
28						28
29						29
30						30
31						31
32						32
33						33
34						34
35						35
36						36
37						37

PROBLEM 4-4A or 4-4B (continued)

GENERAL LEDGER

ACCOUNT _____ ACCOUNT NO. _____

DATE	ITEM	POST. REF.	DEBIT	CREDIT	BALANCE	
					DEBIT	CREDIT

ACCOUNT _____ ACCOUNT NO. _____

DATE	ITEM	POST. REF.	DEBIT	CREDIT	BALANCE	
					DEBIT	CREDIT

ACCOUNT _____ ACCOUNT NO. _____

DATE	ITEM	POST. REF.	DEBIT	CREDIT	BALANCE	
					DEBIT	CREDIT

PROBLEM 4-4A or 4-4B (continued)

GENERAL LEDGER

ACCOUNT _____ ACCOUNT NO. _____

DATE	ITEM	POST. REF.	DEBIT	CREDIT	BALANCE	
					DEBIT	CREDIT

ACCOUNT _____ ACCOUNT NO. _____

DATE	ITEM	POST. REF.	DEBIT	CREDIT	BALANCE	
					DEBIT	CREDIT

ACCOUNT _____ ACCOUNT NO. _____

DATE	ITEM	POST. REF.	DEBIT	CREDIT	BALANCE	
					DEBIT	CREDIT

ACCOUNT _____ ACCOUNT NO. _____

DATE	ITEM	POST. REF.	DEBIT	CREDIT	BALANCE	
					DEBIT	CREDIT

PROBLEM 4-4A or 4-4B (continued)

ACCOUNT _____ ACCOUNT NO. _____

DATE	ITEM	POST. REF.	DEBIT	CREDIT	BALANCE	
					DEBIT	CREDIT

ACCOUNT _____ ACCOUNT NO. _____

DATE	ITEM	POST. REF.	DEBIT	CREDIT	BALANCE	
					DEBIT	CREDIT

ACCOUNT _____ ACCOUNT NO. _____

DATE	ITEM	POST. REF.	DEBIT	CREDIT	BALANCE	
					DEBIT	CREDIT

ACCOUNT _____ ACCOUNT NO. _____

DATE	ITEM	POST. REF.	DEBIT	CREDIT	BALANCE	
					DEBIT	CREDIT

ACCOUNT _____ ACCOUNT NO. _____

DATE	ITEM	POST. REF.	DEBIT	CREDIT	BALANCE	
					DEBIT	CREDIT

PROBLEM 4-4A or 4-4B (concluded)

ACCOUNT _____ ACCOUNT NO. _____

DATE	ITEM	POST. REF.	DEBIT	CREDIT	BALANCE	
					DEBIT	CREDIT

ACCOUNT NAME	DEBIT	CREDIT

Adjustments and the Work Sheet

LEARNING OBJECTIVES

1. Define a fiscal period and a fiscal year.
2. List the classifications of the accounts that occupy each column of a ten-column work sheet.
3. Complete a work sheet for a service-type enterprise, involving adjustments for supplies used, expired insurance, depreciation, and accrued wages.
4. Prepare an income statement, a statement of owner's equity, and a balance sheet for a service-type business directly from the work sheet.
5. Journalize and post the adjusting entries.
6. Prepare an income statement, a statement of owner's equity, and a balance sheet for a business with more than one revenue account and more than one accumulated depreciation account.

KEY TERMS

Accounting cycle
Accrual
Accrued wages
Adjusting entry
Adjustments
Book value
Contra account

Depreciation
Fiscal period or year
Matching principle
Mixed accounts
Straight-line method
Work sheet

STUDY GUIDE QUESTIONS

PART 1   True/False

For each of the following statements, circle T if the statement is true and F if the statement is false.

T   F   1. The purpose of adjustments is to correct balances that are in error.

T   F   2. Adjusting entries recorded on a work sheet must also be journalized.

T   F   3. The purpose of depreciating an asset is to spread out the cost of the asset over its useful life.

T   F   4. The book value of an asset is always equal to the asset's true market value.

T   F   5. The normal balance of Accumulated Depreciation, Equipment, is on the debit side.

T   F   6. Each adjusting entry involves both an income statement account and a balance sheet account.

T   F   7. If the total of the Income Statement Debit column is larger than the total of the Income Statement Credit column, the company must have a net loss.

T   F   8. The purpose of a work sheet is to enable the accountant to prepare the financial statements.

T   F   9. The Drawing account is recorded on a work sheet in the Trial Balance Debit column, the Adjusted Trial Balance Debit column, and the Income Statement Debit column.

T   F   10. The cost of supplies used will appear in the Adjustments Debit column, the Adjusted Trial Balance Debit column, and the Income Statement Debit column.

PART 2   Completion—Language of Business

Complete each of the following statements by writing the appropriate words in the spaces provided.

1. The cost of an asset less the accumulated depreciation is called the _____ .

2. The time span that covers a company's accounting cycle is called its _____ .

3. Since the plus and minus signs on Accumulated Depreciation, Equipment, are the opposite of the signs on Equipment, the Accumulated Depreciation, Equipment, account is called a(n) _____ account.

4. Internal transactions that are used to bring the ledger accounts up to date are called _____ .

5. The amount of unpaid wages owed to employees for the time between the last payday and the end of the fiscal period are called _____ .

6. The _____ represents the steps in the accounting process that are completed during the fiscal period.

7. The Prepaid Insurance and Supplies accounts are called _____ , because their balances that appear in the Trial Balance column consist of partly income statement amounts and partly balance sheet amounts.

8. The _____ requires that the expenses of one period must be related to the revenue of the same period.

9. The term representing loss in usefulness of assets is _____ .

PART 3   Adjusting Entries

Record the adjusting entries directly in the T accounts, and label the other account.

1. Insurance expired, $420.

        Prepaid Insurance

Bal.	830		

2. Supplies inventory, $640.

        Supplies

Bal.	980		

3. Additional depreciation, $2,000.

        Accumulated Depreciation, Equipment

		Bal.	4,100	

4. Accrued wages, $330.

        Wages Expense

Bal.	7,200		

PART 4 Analyzing the Work Sheet

Carry the balances forward from the Trial Balance columns to the appropriate column. The first two accounts are provided as examples.

Account Name	Trial Balance		Adjustments		Adj. Trial Balance		Income Statement		Balance Sheet	
	Debit	Credit	Debit	Credit	Debit	Credit	Debit	Credit	Debit	Credit
0. Equipment	X				X				X	
0. Supplies Expense			X		X		X			
1. Cash	X									
2. C. Dahl, Capital		X								
3. Advertising Expense	X									
4. Accounts Receivable	X									
5. Wages Expense	X									
6. Accumulated Depreciation, Equipment		X								
7. Wages Payable										
8. Supplies	X									
9. C. Dahl, Drawing	X									
10. Service Revenue		X								

DEMONSTRATION PROBLEM

The general ledger of Best Carpenters contains the following account balances as of December 31 of this year:

Cash	$ 2,560	H. Feinberg, Drawing	$60,000
Accounts Receivable	7,428	Income from Services	89,845
Supplies	1,218	Wages Expense	21,500
Prepaid Insurance	960	Rent Expense	4,800
Equipment	4,270	Advertising Expense	1,216
Accumulated Depreciation,		Utilities Expense	1,344
Equipment	1,230	Insurance Expense	0
Truck	21,550	Supplies Expense	0
Accumulated Depreciation, Truck	4,310	Depreciation Expense, Equipment	0
Accounts Payable	426	Depreciation Expense, Truck	0
Wages Payable	0	Miscellaneous Expense	279
H. Feinberg, Capital	31,314		

Since the firm has been in operation for longer than a year, Accumulated Depreciation, Equipment, and Accumulated Depreciation, Truck, have balances that should be included in the trial balance.

Data for the year-end adjustments are as follows:

a. Wages accrued at December 31, $448.
b. Insurance expired during the year, $768.
c. Inventory of supplies at December 31, $679.
d. Depreciation of equipment during the year, $854.
e. Depreciation of truck during the year, $4,310.

Instructions

Complete the work sheet for the year.

SOLUTION

Best Carpenters
Work Sheet
For Year Ended December 31, 19—

	ACCOUNT NAME	TRIAL BALANCE DEBIT	TRIAL BALANCE CREDIT	ADJUSTMENTS DEBIT	ADJUSTMENTS CREDIT
1	Cash	2 5 6 0 00			
2	Accounts Receivable	7 4 2 8 00			
3	Supplies	1 2 1 8 00			(c) 5 3 9 00
4	Prepaid Insurance	9 6 0 00			(b) 7 6 8 00
5	Equipment	4 2 7 0 00			
6	Accumulated Depreciation, Equipment		1 2 3 0 00		(d) 8 5 4 00
7	Truck	21 5 5 0 00			
8	Accumulated Depreciation, Truck		4 3 1 0 00		(e) 4 3 1 0 00
9	Accounts Payable		4 2 6 00		
10	H. Feinberg, Capital		31 3 1 4 00		
11	H. Feinberg, Drawing	60 0 0 0 00			
12	Income from Services		89 8 4 5 00		
13	Wages Expense	21 5 0 0 00		(a) 4 4 8 00	
14	Rent Expense	4 8 0 0 00			
15	Advertising Expense	1 2 1 6 00			
16	Utilities Expense	1 3 4 4 00			
17	Miscellaneous Expense	2 7 9 00			
18		127 1 2 5 00	127 1 2 5 00		
19	Wages Payable				(a) 4 4 8 00
20	Insurance Expense			(b) 7 6 8 00	
21	Supplies Expense			(c) 5 3 9 00	
22	Depreciation Expense, Equipment			(d) 8 5 4 00	
23	Depreciation Expense, Truck			(e) 4 3 1 0 00	
24				6 9 1 9 00	6 9 1 9 00
25	Net Income				
26					
27					
28					
29					
30					
31					
32					
33					
34					
35					
36					
37					

ADJUSTED TRIAL BALANCE		INCOME STATEMENT		BALANCE SHEET		
DEBIT	CREDIT	DEBIT	CREDIT	DEBIT	CREDIT	
2 5 6 0 00				2 5 6 0 00		1
7 4 2 8 00				7 4 2 8 00		2
6 7 9 00				6 7 9 00		3
1 9 2 00				1 9 2 00		4
4 2 7 0 00				4 2 7 0 00		5
	2 0 8 4 00				2 0 8 4 00	6
21 5 5 0 00				21 5 5 0 00		7
	8 6 2 0 00				8 6 2 0 00	8
	4 2 6 00				4 2 6 00	9
	31 3 1 4 00				31 3 1 4 00	10
60 0 0 0 00				60 0 0 0 00		11
	89 8 4 5 00		89 8 4 5 00			12
21 9 4 8 00		21 9 4 8 00				13
4 8 0 0 00		4 8 0 0 00				14
1 2 1 6 00		1 2 1 6 00				15
1 3 4 4 00		1 3 4 4 00				16
2 7 9 00		2 7 9 00				17
						18
	4 4 8 00				4 4 8 00	19
7 6 8 00		7 6 8 00				20
5 3 9 00		5 3 9 00				21
8 5 4 00		8 5 4 00				22
4 3 1 0 00		4 3 1 0 00				23
132 7 3 7 00	132 7 3 7 00	36 0 5 8 00	89 8 4 5 00	96 6 7 9 00	42 8 9 2 00	24
		53 7 8 7 00			53 7 8 7 00	25
		89 8 4 5 00	89 8 4 5 00	96 6 7 9 00	96 6 7 9 00	26
						27
						28
						29
						30
						31
						32
						33
						34
						35
						36
						37

(For Problem 5-1A or 5-1B, see end of book.)

PROBLEM 5-2A or 5-2B
(The completed work sheet for these problems is at the end of the book.)

PROBLEM 5-2A or 5-2B (continued)

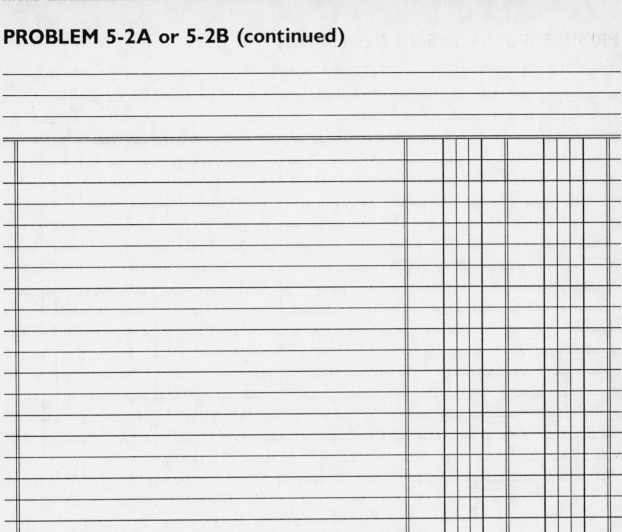

PROBLEM 5-2A or 5-2B (concluded)

GENERAL JOURNAL   PAGE _____

	DATE		DESCRIPTION	POST. REF.	DEBIT	CREDIT	
1							1
2							2
3							3
4							4
5							5
6							6
7							7
8							8
9							9
10							10
11							11
12							12
13							13
14							14
15							15
16							16
17							17

PROBLEM 5-3A or 5-3B
(The work sheet for this problem is at the end of the book.)

PROBLEM 5-3A or 5-3B (continued)

PROBLEM 5-3A or 5-3B (concluded)

GENERAL JOURNAL

PAGE _____

	DATE	DESCRIPTION	POST. REF.	DEBIT	CREDIT	
1						1
2						2
3						3
4						4
5						5
6						6
7						7
8						8
9						9
10						10
11						11
12						12
13						13
14						14
15						15
16						16
17						17
18						18
19						19
20						20
21						21
22						22
23						23
24						24
25						25
26						26
27						27
28						28
29						29
30						30
31						31
32						32
33						33
34						34
35						35
36						36
37						37

PROBLEM 5-4A or 5-4B
(The work sheet for this problem is at the end of the book.)

GENERAL JOURNAL   PAGE _____

	DATE		DESCRIPTION	POST. REF.	DEBIT	CREDIT	
1							1
2							2
3							3
4							4
5							5
6							6
7							7
8							8
9							9
10							10
11							11
12							12
13							13
14							14
15							15
16							16
17							17
18							18
19							19
20							20
21							21
22							22
23							23
24							24
25							25
26							26
27							27
28							28
29							29
30							30
31							31
32							32
33							33
34							34
35							35
36							36
37							37

APPENDIX A

PROBLEM A-1

Year	Depreciation for the Year	Accumulated Depreciation	Book Value

PROBLEM A-2

Year	Depreciation for the Year	Accumulated Depreciation	Book Value

PROBLEM A-3

Year	Depreciation for the Year	Accumulated Depreciation	Book Value

Closing Entries and the Post-Closing Trial Balance

LEARNING OBJECTIVES

1. Recall the steps in the accounting cycle.
2. Journalize and post closing entries for a service-type enterprise.
3. Prepare a post-closing trial balance for any type of enterprise.
4. Define the following methods of accounting: accrual basis, cash-receipts-and-disbursements basis, modified cash basis.
5. Prepare interim statements.

KEY TERMS

Accrual basis
Cash-receipts-and-disbursements basis
Closing entries
Income Summary
Interim statements

Modified cash basis
Nominal or temporary-equity accounts
Post-closing trial balance
Real or permanent accounts

STUDY GUIDE QUESTIONS

PART 1   True/False

For each of the following statements, circle T if the statement is true and F if the statement is false.

T   F   1. The first step in the closing procedure is to close the expense accounts into the Income Summary account.

T   F   2. The post-closing trial balance is final proof that the total of the debit balances equals the total of the credit balances.

T   F   3. After the closing entries have been posted, the final balance of the Capital account is the same as the amount recorded on the last line of the statement of owner's equity.

T   F   4. Generally, the closing procedure is completed by making three entries.

T   F   5. The purpose of the closing entries is to close off the asset and liability accounts, because their balances apply to only one fiscal period.

T   F   6. The total of the expense accounts is recorded in Income Summary as a credit.

T   F.   7. The last step in the closing procedure is to close the Drawing account into the Capital account.

T   F   8. If you have to debit Income Summary to close it, this indicates a net loss.

T   F   9. The Income Summary is an example of a nominal or temporary-equity account.

T   F   10. The post-closing trial balance includes only the balances of real or permanent accounts.

PART 2 Completion—Language of Business

Complete each of the following statements by writing the appropriate words in the space provided.

1. After the closing entries have been journalized and posted, the _____ _____ is prepared as final proof that the accounts are in balance.
2. The accounts that have balances that are carried over to the next fiscal period are called _____ accounts.
3. Financial statements that are prepared during the fiscal period and cover a period of time less than the fiscal period are called _____ statements.
4. The _____ account is brought into existence to have a debit and credit for each closing entry.
5. A journal entry that is made to clear an account or make the balance of that account equal to zero is called a(n) _____ entry.
6. The _____ accounts apply to only one fiscal period and are closed at the end of the fiscal period.
7. An accounting basis by which revenue is only recorded when it is earned and expenses are only recorded when they are incurred is called the _____ .
8. The _____ is an accounting basis by which revenue is only recorded when it is received in cash and most expenses are only recorded when they are paid in cash. Other expenses to be counted that are not paid in cash include Depreciation Expense, Supplies Expense, and Insurance Expense.

PART 3 Closing Entries

Using the following list of account titles, determine the account titles to be debited and credited for the closing entries below.

a. Rent Expense   c. L. Drew, Drawing   e. L. Drew, Capital
b. Service Income   d. Income Summary   f. Wages Expense

	Debit	Credit
1. Close out the balance of the revenue account.	___	___
2. Close out the balances of the expense accounts.	___	___
3. Close out the amount of the net income for the period.	___	___
4. Close out the balance of the Drawing account.	___	___

PART 4 Posting Closing Entries

After the first closing entries have been journalized and posted, the remaining accounts are shown below in T account form. Based on the T accounts, answer the following questions.

Income Summary		J. See, Capital		J. See, Drawing	
Debit	Credit	Debit	Credit	Debit	Credit
46,000	41,000		Bal. 150,000	Bal. 22,000	

1. The amount of the total revenue is $_____ .
2. The amount of the total expenses is $_____ .
3. The amount of the net income or net loss is $_____ .
4. The amount of the total withdrawals is $_____ .
5. The entry to close Income Summary is a debit to _____ , and a credit to _____ .
6. The entry to close J. See, Drawing, is a debit to _____ and a credit to _____ .
7. The amount of the increase or decrease in capital for the period is $_____ _____ .
8. The ending balance of J. See, Capital, is $_____ .

DEMONSTRATION PROBLEM

After the adjusting entries have been posted, the ledger of W. T. Hawkins, a financial planner, contains the following account balances as of December 31:

Cash	$ 3,064
Accounts Receivable	8,450
Supplies	420
Equipment	10,500
Accumulated Depreciation, Equipment	4,200
Accounts Payable	756
W. T. Hawkins, Capital	18,378
W. T. Hawkins, Drawing	80,000
Income Summary	—
Commissions Earned	92,824
Income from Services	23,050
Salary Expense	21,600
Rent Expense	11,200
Supplies Expense	1,215
Depreciation Expense, Equipment	2,100
Miscellaneous Expense	659

Instructions

Record the closing entries in general journal form.

SOLUTION

GENERAL JOURNAL

PAGE _____

DATE		DESCRIPTION	POST. REF.	DEBIT	CREDIT
19—		*Closing Entries*			
Dec.	31	Commissions Earned		92 824 00	
		Income from Services		23 050 00	
		Income Summary			115 874 00
	31	Income Summary		36 774 00	
		Salary Expense			21 600 00
		Rent Expense			11 200 00
		Supplies Expense			1 215 00
		Depreciation Expense, Equipment			2 100 00
		Miscellaneous Expense			659 00
	31	Income Summary		79 100 00	
		W. T. Hawkins, Capital			79 100 00
	31	W. T. Hawkins, Capital		80 000 00	
		W. T. Hawkins, Drawing			80 000 00

PROBLEM 6-1A or 6-1B

Cash		Income Summary

Office Supplies		Professional Fees

Equipment		Salary Expense

Accumulated Depreciation, Equipment		Rent Expense

Accounts Payable		Telephone Expense

Salaries Payable		Office Supplies Expense

, Capital		Depreciation Expense, Equipment

, Drawing		Miscellaneous Expense

PROBLEM 6-1A or 6-1B (concluded)

GENERAL JOURNAL

PAGE _____

	DATE	DESCRIPTION	POST. REF.	DEBIT	CREDIT	
1						1
2						2
3						3
4						4
5						5
6						6
7						7
8						8
9						9
10						10
11						11
12						12
13						13
14						14
15						15
16						16
17						17
18						18
19						19
20						20
21						21
22						22
23						23
24						24
25						25
26						26
27						27
28						28
29						29
30						30
31						31
32						32
33						33
34						34
35						35
36						36
37						37

PROBLEM 6-2A or 6-2B

GENERAL JOURNAL   PAGE _____

	DATE	DESCRIPTION	POST. REF.	DEBIT	CREDIT	
1						1
2						2
3						3
4						4
5						5
6						6
7						7
8						8
9						9
10						10
11						11
12						12
13						13
14						14
15						15
16						16
17						17
18						18
19						19
20						20
21						21
22						22
23						23
24						24
25						25
26						26
27						27
28						28
29						29
30						30
31						31
32						32
33						33
34						34
35						35
36						36
37						37

PROBLEM 6-3A or 6-3B

(The completed work sheets for these problems are at the end of the book.)

GENERAL JOURNAL

	DATE		DESCRIPTION	POST. REF.	DEBIT	CREDIT	
1							1
2							2
3							3
4							4
5							5
6							6
7							7
8							8
9							9
10							10
11							11
12							12
13							13
14							14
15							15
16							16
17							17
18							18
19							19
20							20
21							21
22							22
23							23
24							24
25							25
26							26
27							27
28							28
29							29
30							30
31							31
32							32
33							33
34							34
35							35
36							36

PROBLEM 6-3A or 6-3B (continued)

GENERAL LEDGER

ACCOUNT *Cash* ACCOUNT NO. *111*

DATE	ITEM	POST. REF.	DEBIT	CREDIT	BALANCE	
					DEBIT	CREDIT

ACCOUNT *Office Supplies* ACCOUNT NO. *114*

DATE	ITEM	POST. REF.	DEBIT	CREDIT	BALANCE	
					DEBIT	CREDIT

ACCOUNT *Equipment* ACCOUNT NO. *121*

DATE	ITEM	POST. REF.	DEBIT	CREDIT	BALANCE	
					DEBIT	CREDIT

ACCOUNT *Accumulated Depreciation, Equipment* ACCOUNT NO. *122*

DATE	ITEM	POST. REF.	DEBIT	CREDIT	BALANCE	
					DEBIT	CREDIT

ACCOUNT *Salaries Payable* ACCOUNT NO. *212*

DATE	ITEM	POST. REF.	DEBIT	CREDIT	BALANCE	
					DEBIT	CREDIT

PROBLEM 6-3A or 6-3B (continued)

ACCOUNT _____ , Capital _____ ACCOUNT NO. ___ 311

DATE	ITEM	POST. REF.	DEBIT	CREDIT	BALANCE	
					DEBIT	CREDIT

ACCOUNT _____ , Drawing _____ ACCOUNT NO. ___ 312

DATE	ITEM	POST. REF.	DEBIT	CREDIT	BALANCE	
					DEBIT	CREDIT

ACCOUNT ___ Income Summary _____ ACCOUNT NO. ___ 313

DATE	ITEM	POST. REF.	DEBIT	CREDIT	BALANCE	
					DEBIT	CREDIT

ACCOUNT _____ Earned _____ ACCOUNT NO. ___ 411

DATE	ITEM	POST. REF.	DEBIT	CREDIT	BALANCE	
					DEBIT	CREDIT

PROBLEM 6-3A or 6-3B (continued)

ACCOUNT _Salary Expense_ _____ ACCOUNT NO. _511_

DATE	ITEM	POST. REF.	DEBIT	CREDIT	BALANCE	
					DEBIT	CREDIT

ACCOUNT _Rent Expense_ _____ ACCOUNT NO. _512_

DATE	ITEM	POST. REF.	DEBIT	CREDIT	BALANCE	
					DEBIT	CREDIT

ACCOUNT _Office Supplies Expense_ _____ ACCOUNT NO. _513_

DATE	ITEM	POST. REF.	DEBIT	CREDIT	BALANCE	
					DEBIT	CREDIT

ACCOUNT _Depreciation Expense, Equipment_ _____ ACCOUNT NO. _514_

DATE	ITEM	POST. REF.	DEBIT	CREDIT	BALANCE	
					DEBIT	CREDIT

PROBLEM 6-3A or 6-3B (continued)

ACCOUNT _Telephone Expense_ _____ ACCOUNT NO. _515_

DATE	ITEM	POST. REF.	DEBIT	CREDIT	BALANCE	
					DEBIT	CREDIT

ACCOUNT _Advertising Expense_ _____ ACCOUNT NO. _516_

DATE	ITEM	POST. REF.	DEBIT	CREDIT	BALANCE	
					DEBIT	CREDIT

ACCOUNT _Miscellaneous Expense_ _____ ACCOUNT NO. _519_

DATE	ITEM	POST. REF.	DEBIT	CREDIT	BALANCE	
					DEBIT	CREDIT

PROBLEM 6-3A or 6-3B (concluded)

ACCOUNT NAME	DEBIT	CREDIT

PROBLEM 6-4A or 6-4B
(The work sheets for these problems are at the end of the book.)

PROBLEM 6-4A or 6-4B (continued)

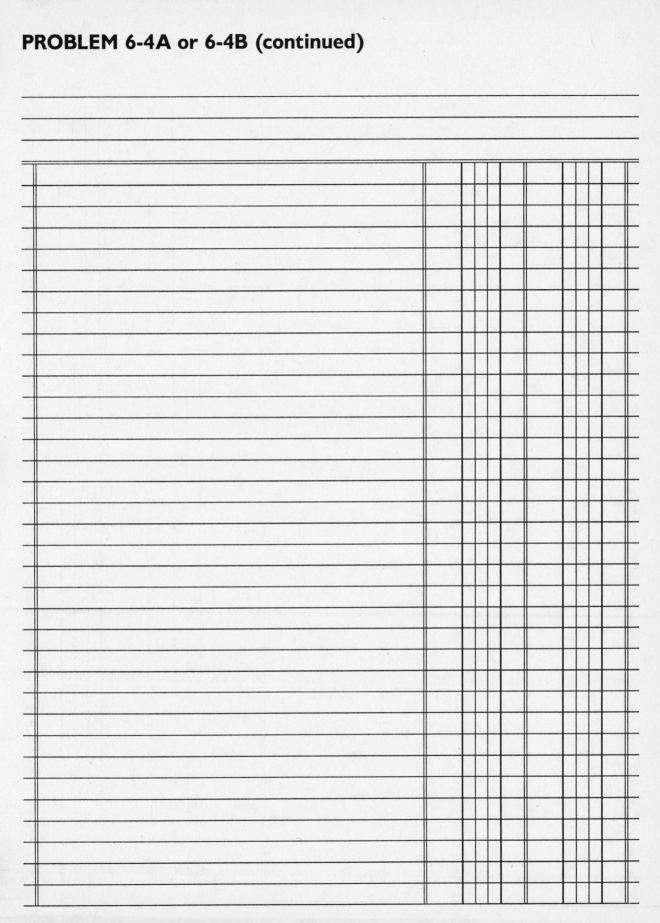

PROBLEM 6-4A or 6-4B (concluded)

GENERAL JOURNAL

PAGE _____

	DATE		DESCRIPTION	POST. REF.	DEBIT	CREDIT	
1							1
2							2
3							3
4							4
5							5
6							6
7							7
8							8
9							9
10							10
11							11
12							12
13							13
14							14
15							15
16							16
17							17
18							18
19							19
20							20
21							21
22							22
23							23
24							24
25							25
26							26
27							27
28							28
29							29
30							30
31							31
32							32
33							33
34							34
35							35
36							36
37							37

ACCOUNTING CYCLE REVIEW PROBLEM (See work sheet at end of book.)

GENERAL JOURNAL   PAGE _____

	DATE		DESCRIPTION	POST. REF.	DEBIT	CREDIT	
1							1
2							2
3							3
4							4
5							5
6							6
7							7
8							8
9							9
10							10
11							11
12							12
13							13
14							14
15							15
16							16
17							17
18							18
19							19
20							20
21							21
22							22
23							23
24							24
25							25
26							26
27							27
28							28
29							29
30							30
31							31
32							32
33							33
34							34
35							35
36							36

ACCOUNTING CYCLE REVIEW PROBLEM (continued)

GENERAL JOURNAL

PAGE _____

	DATE	DESCRIPTION	POST. REF.	DEBIT	CREDIT	
1						1
2						2
3						3
4						4
5						5
6						6
7						7
8						8
9						9
10						10
11						11
12						12
13						13
14						14
15						15
16						16
17						17
18						18
19						19
20						20
21						21
22						22
23						23
24						24
25						25
26						26
27						27
28						28
29						29
30						30
31						31
32						32
33						33
34						34
35						35
36						36
37						37

ACCOUNTING CYCLE REVIEW PROBLEM (continued)

GENERAL JOURNAL   PAGE _____

	DATE		DESCRIPTION	POST. REF.	DEBIT	CREDIT	
1							1
2							2
3							3
4							4
5							5
6							6
7							7
8							8
9							9
10							10
11							11
12							12
13							13
14							14
15							15
16							16
17							17
18							18
19							19
20							20
21							21
22							22
23							23
24							24
25							25
26							26
27							27
28							28
29							29
30							30
31							31
32							32
33							33
34							34
35							35
36							36
37							37

ACCOUNTING CYCLE REVIEW PROBLEM (continued)

GENERAL JOURNAL

PAGE _____

	DATE	DESCRIPTION	POST. REF.	DEBIT	CREDIT	
1						1
2						2
3						3
4						4
5						5
6						6
7						7
8						8
9						9
10						10
11						11
12						12
13						13
14						14
15						15
16						16
17						17
18						18
19						19
20						20
21						21
22						22
23						23
24						24
25						25
26						26
27						27
28						28
29						29
30						30
31						31
32						32
33						33
34						34
35						35
36						36
37						37

ACCOUNTING CYCLE REVIEW PROBLEM (continued)

GENERAL JOURNAL

PAGE _____

	DATE	DESCRIPTION	POST. REF.	DEBIT	CREDIT	
1						1
2						2
3						3
4						4
5						5
6						6
7						7
8						8
9						9
10						10
11						11
12						12
13						13
14						14
15						15
16						16
17						17
18						18
19						19
20						20
21						21
22						22
23						23
24						24
25						25
26						26
27						27
28						28
29						29
30						30
31						31
32						32
33						33
34						34
35						35
36						36
37						37

ACCOUNTING CYCLE REVIEW PROBLEM (continued)

GENERAL JOURNAL

	DATE	DESCRIPTION	POST. REF.	DEBIT	CREDIT	
1						1
2						2
3						3
4						4
5						5
6						6
7						7
8						8
9						9
10						10
11						11
12						12
13						13
14						14
15						15
16						16
17						17
18						18
19						19
20						20
21						21
22						22
23						23
24						24
25						25
26						26
27						27
28						28
29						29
30						30
31						31
32						32
33						33
34						34
35						35
36						36
37						37

ACCOUNTING CYCLE REVIEW PROBLEM (continued)

GENERAL LEDGER

ACCOUNT *Cash*   ACCOUNT NO. *111*

DATE	ITEM	POST. REF.	DEBIT	CREDIT	BALANCE	
					DEBIT	CREDIT

ACCOUNT *Accounts Receivable*   ACCOUNT NO. *112*

DATE	ITEM	POST. REF.	DEBIT	CREDIT	BALANCE	
					DEBIT	CREDIT

ACCOUNTING CYCLE REVIEW PROBLEM (continued)

ACCOUNT _Supplies_ ACCOUNT NO. _113_

DATE	ITEM	POST. REF.	DEBIT	CREDIT	BALANCE	
					DEBIT	CREDIT

ACCOUNT _Prepaid Insurance_ ACCOUNT NO. _114_

DATE	ITEM	POST. REF.	DEBIT	CREDIT	BALANCE	
					DEBIT	CREDIT

ACCOUNT _Land_ ACCOUNT NO. _121_

DATE	ITEM	POST. REF.	DEBIT	CREDIT	BALANCE	
					DEBIT	CREDIT

ACCOUNT _Building_ ACCOUNT NO. _122_

DATE	ITEM	POST. REF.	DEBIT	CREDIT	BALANCE	
					DEBIT	CREDIT

ACCOUNTING CYCLE REVIEW PROBLEM (continued)

ACCOUNT _Accumulated Depreciation, Building_ _____ ACCOUNT NO. _123_

DATE	ITEM	POST. REF.	DEBIT	CREDIT	BALANCE	
					DEBIT	CREDIT

ACCOUNT _Pool/Slide Facility_ _____ ACCOUNT NO. _124_

DATE	ITEM	POST. REF.	DEBIT	CREDIT	BALANCE	
					DEBIT	CREDIT

ACCOUNT _Accumulated Depreciation, Pool/Slide Facility_ _____ ACCOUNT NO. _125_

DATE	ITEM	POST. REF.	DEBIT	CREDIT	BALANCE	
					DEBIT	CREDIT

ACCOUNT _Pool Furniture_ _____ ACCOUNT NO. _126_

DATE	ITEM	POST. REF.	DEBIT	CREDIT	BALANCE	
					DEBIT	CREDIT

ACCOUNTING CYCLE REVIEW PROBLEM (continued)

ACCOUNT *Accumulated Depreciation, Pool Furniture* ACCOUNT NO. *127*

DATE	ITEM	POST. REF.	DEBIT	CREDIT	BALANCE DEBIT	BALANCE CREDIT

ACCOUNT *Accounts Payable* ACCOUNT NO. *211*

DATE	ITEM	POST. REF.	DEBIT	CREDIT	BALANCE DEBIT	BALANCE CREDIT

ACCOUNT *Wages Payable* ACCOUNT NO. *212*

DATE	ITEM	POST. REF.	DEBIT	CREDIT	BALANCE DEBIT	BALANCE CREDIT

ACCOUNTING CYCLE REVIEW PROBLEM (continued)

ACCOUNT *Mortgage Payable*   ACCOUNT NO. *221*

DATE	ITEM	POST. REF.	DEBIT	CREDIT	BALANCE	
					DEBIT	CREDIT

ACCOUNT *K. Taylor, Capital*   ACCOUNT NO. *311*

DATE	ITEM	POST. REF.	DEBIT	CREDIT	BALANCE	
					DEBIT	CREDIT

ACCOUNT *K. Taylor, Drawing*   ACCOUNT NO. *312*

DATE	ITEM	POST. REF.	DEBIT	CREDIT	BALANCE	
					DEBIT	CREDIT

ACCOUNT *Income Summary*   ACCOUNT NO. *313*

DATE	ITEM	POST. REF.	DEBIT	CREDIT	BALANCE	
					DEBIT	CREDIT

ACCOUNTING CYCLE REVIEW PROBLEM (continued)

ACCOUNT *Income from Services*   ACCOUNT NO. *411*

DATE		ITEM	POST. REF.	DEBIT	CREDIT	BALANCE	
						DEBIT	CREDIT

ACCOUNT *Concession Income*   ACCOUNT NO. *412*

DATE		ITEM	POST. REF.	DEBIT	CREDIT	BALANCE	
						DEBIT	CREDIT

ACCOUNT *Pool Maintenance Expense*   ACCOUNT NO. *511*

DATE		ITEM	POST. REF.	DEBIT	CREDIT	BALANCE	
						DEBIT	CREDIT

ACCOUNT *Wages Expense*   ACCOUNT NO. *512*

DATE		ITEM	POST. REF.	DEBIT	CREDIT	BALANCE	
						DEBIT	CREDIT

ACCOUNTING CYCLE REVIEW PROBLEM (continued)

ACCOUNT *Advertising Expense* _____ ACCOUNT NO. *513*

DATE	ITEM	POST. REF.	DEBIT	CREDIT	BALANCE DEBIT	BALANCE CREDIT

ACCOUNT *Utilities Expense* _____ ACCOUNT NO. *514*

DATE	ITEM	POST. REF.	DEBIT	CREDIT	BALANCE DEBIT	BALANCE CREDIT

ACCOUNT *Interest Expense* _____ ACCOUNT NO. *515*

DATE	ITEM	POST. REF.	DEBIT	CREDIT	BALANCE DEBIT	BALANCE CREDIT

ACCOUNT *Supplies Expense* _____ ACCOUNT NO. *516*

DATE	ITEM	POST. REF.	DEBIT	CREDIT	BALANCE DEBIT	BALANCE CREDIT

ACCOUNTING CYCLE REVIEW PROBLEM (continued)

ACCOUNT _Insurance Expense_   ACCOUNT NO. _517_

DATE	ITEM	POST. REF.	DEBIT	CREDIT	BALANCE	
					DEBIT	CREDIT

ACCOUNT _Depreciation Expense, Building_   ACCOUNT NO. _518_

DATE	ITEM	POST. REF.	DEBIT	CREDIT	BALANCE	
					DEBIT	CREDIT

ACCOUNT _Depreciation Expense, Pool/Slide Facility_   ACCOUNT NO. _519_

DATE	ITEM	POST. REF.	DEBIT	CREDIT	BALANCE	
					DEBIT	CREDIT

ACCOUNT _Depreciation Expense, Pool Furniture_   ACCOUNT NO. _520_

DATE	ITEM	POST. REF.	DEBIT	CREDIT	BALANCE	
					DEBIT	CREDIT

ACCOUNTING CYCLE REVIEW PROBLEM (continued)

ACCOUNT *Miscellaneous Expense*　　　　ACCOUNT NO. 522

DATE	ITEM	POST. REF.	DEBIT	CREDIT	BALANCE DEBIT	BALANCE CREDIT

ACCOUNTING CYCLE REVIEW PROBLEM (continued)

● ACCOUNTING CYCLE REVIEW PROBLEM (continued)

ACCOUNTING CYCLE REVIEW PROBLEM (concluded)

ACCOUNT NAME	DEBIT	CREDIT

7 Accounting for Professional Enterprises: The Combined Journal (Optional)

LEARNING OBJECTIVES

1. Describe the accounting records for a professional enterprise.
2. Record transactions for both a professional and a service-type enterprise in a combined journal.
3. Post from the combined journal and determine the cash balance.
4. Prepare a work sheet for a professional enterprise.
5. Prepare financial statements for a professional enterprise.
6. Record adjusting and closing entries in a combined journal.

KEY TERMS

Combined journal
Patient's ledger record

Professional enterprise
Special columns

STUDY GUIDE QUESTIONS

PART 1   True/False

For each of the following statements, circle T if the statement is true and F if the statement is false.

T   F   1. Each amount in the Other Accounts Credit column is posted individually.

T   F   2. If a combined journal is in use, it is not necessary to have a general journal.

T   F   3. In recording a transaction in a combined journal, if the Account Name column is left blank, an error must have been made.

T   F   4. The totals of the Other Accounts Debit and Credit columns are posted at the end of the month.

T   F   5. In a combined journal, all the special columns are posted as totals at the end of the month.

T   F   6. The procedures for preparing the work sheet and the financial statements are the same for a professional enterprise and a service business.

T   F   7. A dash in the Posting Reference column of a combined journal indicates that each amount in the special columns is posted individually.

T   F   8. The Other Accounts Debit and Credit columns of the combined journal can be used to record the closing entries.

T   F   9. In a combined journal, an X in parentheses below a total indicates that the total has been posted.

T   F   10. In a combined journal, the posting reference for the total of a special column is placed in parentheses below the column total.

PART 2 Chart of Accounts

C. C. Pietro, the owner of Pietro Rental Agency, has asked you to set up a tentative chart of accounts for her business. She rents spaces in a shopping center and has two employees. The company's revenue is in the form of commissions on rentals. The owner and the employees use their own cars to inspect and show properties and are reimbursed on a mileage basis. The company receives deposits from clients and forwards these amounts to the property owners. Extensive use is made of advertising.

Chart of Accounts

Assets

Liabilities

Owner's Equity

Revenue

Expenses

PART 3 Combined Journal

C. C. Pietro decides to use a combined journal. Make a tentative list of the headings for the special columns for a combined journal.

_____

_____

_____

_____

_____

_____

_____

DEMONSTRATION PROBLEM

Transactions for Clark's Cleaners are presented below. (These are the same transactions as described in the first three chapters.) Assume the posting has been completed.

June   1 N. L. Clark invests $40,000 cash in his new business.
        2 Buys equipment costing $22,000, paying cash (Ck. No. 1).
        2 Buys equipment costing $4,000 on credit from Drake Equipment Company.
        5 Pays $1,000 to Drake Equipment Company to be applied against the firm's liability of $4,000 (Ck. No. 2).
        5 Buys cleaning fluid and garment bags on account from Blair Supply Company for $400.
        7 Cash revenue received for the first week, $960.
        8 Pays rent for the month, $500 (Ck. No. 3).
       10 Pays wages to a part-time employee, for the period June 1 through June 10, $440 (Ck. No. 4).
       11 Pays $360 for a two-year liability insurance policy (Ck. No. 5).
       14 Cash revenue received for the second week, $980.
       14 Receives bill from the _City News_ for newspaper advertising, $180.
       15 Pays $1,800 to Drake Equipment Company as part payment on account (Ck. No. 6).
       15 Receives and pays bills for utilities, $220 (Ck. No. 7).
       15 Pays $180 to _City News_ for advertising (Ck. No. 8). (This bill has been previously recorded.)
       21 Cash revenue received for the third week, $830.
       23 Clark's Cleaners enters into a contract with Formal Rentals to clean their for-hire formal garments on a credit basis. Clark's Cleaners bills Formal Rentals for services performed, $140.
       24 Pays wages to part-time employee, $490, for June 11 through June 24 (Ck. No. 9).
       26 Buys additional equipment for $940 from Drake Equipment Company, paying $140 down, with the remaining $800 on account (Ck. No. 10).
       30 Cash received for the remainder of the month, $960.
       30 Receives $90 from Formal Rentals to apply on amount previously billed.
       30 Clark withdraws $1,200 in cash for personal use (Ck. No. 11).

Instructions

Record the June transactions in a combined journal.

SOLUTION

Notice the first transaction of June 5 involving payment to a creditor on account. The name of the creditor is recorded in the Account Name column. Likewise, in receiving cash from a customer on account (second entry of June 30), the name of the charge customer is recorded in the Account Name column.

COMBINED

	CASH		CK. NO.	DATE		ACCOUNT NAME	POST. REF.	OTHER ACCOUNTS	
	DEBIT	CREDIT						DEBIT	CREDIT
1				19—					
2	40 000 00			June	1	N. L. Clark, Capital			40 000 00
3		22 000 00	1		2	Equipment		22 000 00	
4					2	Equipment		4 000 00	
5		1 000 00	2		5	Drake Equipment Co.	—		
6					5	Supplies		4 00 00	
7	9 60 00				7	————	—		
8		5 00 00	3		8	Rent Expense		5 00 00	
9		4 40 00	4		10	————	—		
10		3 60 00	5		11	Prepaid Insurance		3 60 00	
11	9 80 00				14	————	—		
12					14	Advertising Expense		1 80 00	
13		1 800 00	6		15	Drake Equipment Co.	—		
14		2 20 00	7		15	Utilities Expense		2 20 00	
15		1 80 00	8		15	City News	—		
16	8 30 00				21	————	—		
17					23	Formal Rentals	—		
18		4 90 00	9		24	————	—		
19		1 40 00	10		26	Equipment		9 40 00	
20	9 60 00				30	————	—		
21	9 00 00				30	Formal Rentals	—		
22		1 200 00	11		30	N. L. Clark, Drawing		1 200 00	
23	43 820 00	28 330 00			30			29 800 00	40 000 00
24									
25									

126

JOURNAL

	ACCOUNTS RECEIVABLE		ACCOUNTS PAYABLE		INCOME FROM SERVICES	WAGES EXPENSE	
	DEBIT	CREDIT	DEBIT	CREDIT	CREDIT	DEBIT	
1							
2							
3							
4				4 0 0 0 00			
5			1 0 0 0 00				
6				4 0 0 00			
7					9 6 0 00		
8							
9						4 4 0 00	
10							
11					9 8 0 00		
12				1 8 0 00			
13			1 8 0 0 00				
14							
15				1 8 0 00			
16					8 3 0 00		
17	1 4 0 00				1 4 0 00		
18						4 9 0 00	
19				8 0 0 00			
20					9 6 0 00		
21		9 0 00					
22							
23	1 4 0 00	9 0 00	2 9 8 0 00	5 3 8 0 00	3 8 7 0 00	9 3 0 00	
24							
25							

(Problem 7-1A and 7-1B and Problem 7-2A and 7-2B combined journals are at the end of the book.)

PROBLEM 7-3A or 7-3B

(The combined journal for this problem is at the end of the book.)

GENERAL LEDGER

ACCOUNT *Cash* _____ ACCOUNT NO. *111*

DATE		ITEM	POST. REF.	DEBIT	CREDIT	BALANCE	
						DEBIT	CREDIT
19—							
Aug.	31	Balance	✓			6 2 8 8 00	

ACCOUNT *Accounts Receivable* _____ ACCOUNT NO. *112*

DATE		ITEM	POST. REF.	DEBIT	CREDIT	BALANCE	
						DEBIT	CREDIT
19—							
Aug.	31	Balance	✓			4 4 9 6 00	

ACCOUNT *Supplies* _____ ACCOUNT NO. *113*

DATE		ITEM	POST. REF.	DEBIT	CREDIT	BALANCE	
						DEBIT	CREDIT
19—							
Aug.	31	Balance	✓			2 2 8 0 00	

ACCOUNT *Prepaid Insurance* _____ ACCOUNT NO. *114*

DATE		ITEM	POST. REF.	DEBIT	CREDIT	BALANCE	
						DEBIT	CREDIT
19—							
Aug.	31	Balance	✓			3 6 0 0 00	

ACCOUNT *Equipment* _____ ACCOUNT NO. *121*

DATE		ITEM	POST. REF.	DEBIT	CREDIT	BALANCE	
						DEBIT	CREDIT
19—							
Aug.	31	Balance	✓			18 9 2 0 00	

PROBLEM 7-3A or 7-3B (continued)

ACCOUNT _Accumulated Depreciation, Equipment_ ACCOUNT NO. _122_

DATE		ITEM	POST. REF.	DEBIT	CREDIT	BALANCE	
						DEBIT	CREDIT
19—							
Aug.	31	Balance	√				10 3 6 2 00

ACCOUNT _Accounts Payable_ ACCOUNT NO. _211_

DATE		ITEM	POST. REF.	DEBIT	CREDIT	BALANCE	
						DEBIT	CREDIT
19—							
Aug.	31	Balance	√				3 2 0 50

ACCOUNT _____ ACCOUNT NO. _311_

DATE		ITEM	POST. REF.	DEBIT	CREDIT	BALANCE	
						DEBIT	CREDIT
19—							
Aug.	31	Balance	√				40 1 1 5 00

ACCOUNT _____ ACCOUNT NO. _312_

DATE		ITEM	POST. REF.	DEBIT	CREDIT	BALANCE	
						DEBIT	CREDIT
19—							
Aug.	31	Balance	√			16 7 5 0 00	

ACCOUNT _Income Summary_ ACCOUNT NO. _313_

DATE	ITEM	POST. REF.	DEBIT	CREDIT	BALANCE	
					DEBIT	CREDIT

PROBLEM 7-3A or 7-3B (continued)

ACCOUNT _Professional Fees_   ACCOUNT NO. _411_

DATE		ITEM	POST. REF.	DEBIT	CREDIT	BALANCE	
						DEBIT	CREDIT
19—							
Aug.	31	Balance	√				33 1 0 0 00

ACCOUNT _Salary Expense_   ACCOUNT NO. _511_

DATE		ITEM	POST. REF.	DEBIT	CREDIT	BALANCE	
						DEBIT	CREDIT
19—							
Aug.	31	Balance	√			17 3 5 0 00	

ACCOUNT _Rent Expense_   ACCOUNT NO. _512_

DATE		ITEM	POST. REF.	DEBIT	CREDIT	BALANCE	
						DEBIT	CREDIT
19—							
Aug.	31	Balance	√			7 2 0 0 00	

ACCOUNT _Laboratory Expense_   ACCOUNT NO. _513_

DATE		ITEM	POST. REF.	DEBIT	CREDIT	BALANCE	
						DEBIT	CREDIT
19—							
Aug.	31	Balance	√			4 2 5 0 00	

PROBLEM 7-3A or 7-3B (continued)

ACCOUNT *Utilities Expense*   ACCOUNT NO. *514*

DATE		ITEM	POST. REF.	DEBIT	CREDIT	BALANCE	
						DEBIT	CREDIT
19—							
Aug.	31	Balance	√			1 76 5 50	

ACCOUNT *Depreciation Expense, Equipment*   ACCOUNT NO. *515*

DATE	ITEM	POST. REF.	DEBIT	CREDIT	BALANCE	
					DEBIT	CREDIT

ACCOUNT *Miscellaneous Expense*   ACCOUNT NO. *516*

DATE		ITEM	POST. REF.	DEBIT	CREDIT	BALANCE	
						DEBIT	CREDIT
19—							
Aug.	31	Balance	√			9 9 8 00	

PROBLEM 7-3A or 7-3B (concluded)

_____

_____

_____

ACCOUNT NAME	DEBIT	CREDIT

PROBLEM 7-4A or 7-4B

(The combined journal for this problem is at the end of the book.)

Chart of Accounts

Assets

Revenue

Expenses

Liabilities

Owner's Equity

Bank Accounts and Cash Funds

LEARNING OBJECTIVES

1. Describe the procedure for depositing checks.
2. Reconcile a bank statement.
3. Record the required journal entries directly from the bank reconciliation.
4. Record journal entries to establish and reimburse Petty Cash Fund.
5. Complete petty cash vouchers and petty cash payments records.
6. Record the journal entries to establish a Change Fund.
7. Record journal entries for transactions involving Cash Short and Over.

KEY TERMS

ABA number	Endorsement
ATM	Ledger balance of cash
Bank reconciliation	MICR
Bank statement	NSF (Not Sufficient Funds) checks
Blank endorsement	Outstanding checks
Canceled checks	Payee
Cash funds	Petty Cash Fund
Change Fund	Petty cash payments record
Check writer	Petty cash voucher
Collections	Promissory note
Denominations	Qualified endorsement
Deposit in transit	Restrictive endorsement
Deposit slips	Service charge
Drawer	Signature card

STUDY GUIDE QUESTIONS

PART 1 True/False

For each of the following statements, circle T if the statement is true and F if the statement is false:

T F 1. Cash received by mail should be deposited by the same person who accepts and lists it.

T F 2. Each petty cash payment is entered separately in the general journal.

T F 3. If the final balance of Cash Short and Over is a debit balance, it is treated as a deduction from Sales.

T F 4. A qualified endorsement prevents any further transferring of a check by signing over the check from one person to another.

T F 5. On a bank reconciliation, outstanding checks are deducted from the bank statement balance.

T F 6. Payments made from the petty cash fund are journalized when the petty cash fund is reimbursed.

T F 7. A credit memo increases the depositor's bank balance.

T F   8. The entry to reimburse the Petty Cash Fund involves a debit to Petty Cash Fund and a credit to Cash.

T F   9. The entry for an NSF check involves a debit to Accounts Payable and a credit to Cash.

T F   10. A credit balance in the Cash Short and Over account is listed on the income statement under Miscellaneous Expense.

PART 2 Completion—Language of Business

Complete each of the following statements by writing the appropriate word(s) in the spaces provided:

1. The party to whom a check is made out is called the _____ .
2. The amount that the bank charges a depositor for handling checks and collections is called a(n) _____ .
3. The method used to transfer title of a check is known as a(n) _____ .
4. Varieties of coins and currency are called _____ .
5. Checks issued by the depositor that have been paid by the bank and included with the bank statement are called _____ .
6. An endorsement that prevents further circulation of a check is called a(n) _____ .
7. The party who writes the check is called the _____ .
8. On a bank statement, the balance of the Cash account in the general ledger is called the _____ .
9. A deposit not recorded on the bank statement, because the deposit was made between the bank's cut-off date and the time the statement is received, is called a(n) _____ .
10. The _____ is a cash fund used to handle transactions where customers pay cash for goods and services.
11. An endorsement of a check that contains the words "without recourse" is called a(n) _____ .
12. The procedure used to determine why there is a difference between the balance of Cash in the company's general ledger and in the company's bank records is called a(n) _____ .
13. _____ are checks that have been written by the depositor and deducted on the depositor's records but have not yet reached the bank for payment.
14. In a(n) _____ , the holder (payee) of a check simply signs her or his name on the back of the check.

PART 3   Reimbursing the Petty Cash Fund

Quality Bakery has the petty cash payments record shown on the next page. The amount of the debit balance of the Petty Cash Fund account is $ _____ . Record the entry in general journal form to reimburse the Petty Cash Fund.

GENERAL JOURNAL   PAGE _____

	DATE	DESCRIPTION	POST. REF.	DEBIT	CREDIT	
1						1
2						2
3						3
4						4
5						5
6						6
7						7
8						8
9						9
10						10
11						11
12						12
13						13

PETTY CASH PAYMENTS RECORD

PERIOD OF TIME June 19—

| | | | | DISTRIBUTION OF PAYMENTS | | | OTHER | |
DATE	VOU. NO.	EXPLANATION	PAYMENTS	REPAIR EXPENSE	DELIVERY EXPENSE	MISCELLANEOUS EXPENSE	ACCOUNT	AMOUNT
19—								
June 3	1	H. Ball	7 00				H. Ball, Drawing	7 00
7	2	Marking pens	5 16			5 16		
9	3	Ben's Delivery	4 20		4 20			
12	4	Lightbulbs	6 32			6 32		
17	5	Postage stamps	5 00			5 00		
21	6	Repair fuses	7 10	7 10				
29	7	H. Ball	4 50				H. Ball, Drawing	4 50
30		Totals	39 28	7 10	4 20	16 48		11 50
		Balance in fund $20.72						
		Reimbursed Ck. No. 711 $39.28						
		Total $60.00						

DEMONSTRATION PROBLEM

The Mills Company made the following transactions during June of this year, involving its Petty Cash Fund, its Change Fund, its Cash Short and Over account, and its Income from Services account, received in cash:

June 1 Established a Change Fund, $200.

3 Established a Petty Cash Fund, $100.

14 Recorded cash revenue for period June 1 through 14: cash register tape, $4,980.21; cash count, $5,175.39.

30 Reimbursed the Petty Cash Fund, $94. The petty cash payments record indicated the following expenditures: Supplies, $32; Delivery Expense, $16; Advertising Expense, $35; Miscellaneous Expense, $11.

30 Recorded cash revenue for period June 15 through 30; cash register tape, $5,239.16; cash count, $5,441.09.

30 Recorded an NSF check received from J. Blakely listed on the bank reconciliation, $157.

Instructions

Record the transactions in general journal form.

SOLUTION

GENERAL JOURNAL

PAGE _____

DATE		DESCRIPTION	POST. REF.	DEBIT	CREDIT
19—					
June	1	Change Fund		2 0 0 00	
		Cash			2 0 0 00
		Established a Change Fund.			
	3	Petty Cash Fund		1 0 0 00	
		Cash			1 0 0 00
		Established a Petty Cash Fund.			
	14	Cash		4 9 7 5 39	
		Cash Short and Over		4 82	
		Income from Services			4 9 8 0 21
		To record revenue for period			
		June 1 through 14 involving a			
		cash shortage of $4.82.			
	30	Supplies		3 2 00	
		Delivery Expense		1 6 00	
		Advertising Expense		3 5 00	
		Miscellaneous Expense		1 1 00	
		Cash			9 4 00
		Reimbursed the Petty Cash			
		Fund.			
	30	Cash		5 2 4 1 09	
		Income from Services			5 2 3 9 16
		Cash Short and Over			1 93
		To record revenue for period			
		June 15 through 30 involving			
		a cash overage of $1.93.			
	30	Accounts Receivable		1 5 7 00	
		Cash			1 5 7 00
		To record an NSF check			
		received from J. Blakely.			

PROBLEM 8-1A or 8-1B

Bank Reconciliation

Bank Statement Balance	$
Add:	
	$
Deduct:	
	$
Adjusted Bank Statement Balance	$
Ledger Balance of Cash	$
Add:	$
	$
Deduct:	
Adjusted Ledger Balance of Cash	$

GENERAL JOURNAL

PAGE _____

	DATE	DESCRIPTION	POST. REF.	DEBIT	CREDIT	
1						1
2						2
3						3
4						4
5						5
6						6
7						7
8						8
9						9
10						10
11						11
12						12
13						13
14						14
15						15

PROBLEM 8-2A or 8-2B

GENERAL JOURNAL   PAGE _____

	DATE		DESCRIPTION	POST. REF.	DEBIT	CREDIT	
1							1
2							2
3							3
4							4
5							5
6							6
7							7
8							8
9							9
10							10
11							11
12							12
13							13
14							14
15							15
16							16
17							17
18							18
19							19
20							20
21							21
22							22
23							23
24							24
25							25
26							26
27							27
28							28
29							29
30							30
31							31
32							32
33							33
34							34
35							35
36							36
37							37

PROBLEM 8-2A or 8-2B (concluded)

PETTY CASH PAYMENTS RECORD

DATE	VOU. NO.	EXPLANATION	PAYMENTS	DISTRIBUTION OF PAYMENTS					
				OFFICE SUPPLIES	DELIVERY EXPENSE	MISCELLANEOUS EXPENSE	OTHER ACCOUNTS		
							ACCOUNT	AMOUNT	
1									1
2									2
3									3
4									4
5									5
6									6
7									7
8									8
9									9
10									10
11									11
12									12
13									13
14									14
15									15
16									16
17									17
18									18
19									19
20									20
21									21
22									22
23									23
24									24
25									25

PROBLEM 8-3A or 8-3B

GENERAL JOURNAL

	DATE	DESCRIPTION	POST. REF.	DEBIT	CREDIT	
1						1
2						2
3						3
4						4
5						5
6						6
7						7
8						8
9						9
10						10
11						11
12						12
13						13
14						14
15						15
16						16
17						17
18						18
19						19
20						20
21						21
22						22
23						23
24						24
25						25
26						26
27						27
28						28
29						29
30						30
31						31
32						32
33						33
34						34
35						35
36						36
37						37

PROBLEM 8-4A or 8-4B

Bank Reconciliation
September 30, 19—

Bank Statement Balance		$
Add:		
		_____
		$
Deduct:		
	$	
	_____	_____
Adjusted Bank Statement Balance		$
Ledger Balance of Cash		$
Add:		
		_____
		$
Deduct:	$	
	_____	_____
Adjusted Ledger Balance of Cash		$

GENERAL JOURNAL   PAGE _____

	DATE	DESCRIPTION	POST. REF.	DEBIT	CREDIT	
1						1
2						2
3						3
4						4
5						5
6						6
7						7
8						8
9						9
10						10
11						11
12						12
13						13
14						14
15						15

PROBLEM 8-4A or 8-4B (concluded)

THIS FORM IS PROVIDED TO HELP YOU BALANCE YOUR BANK STATEMENT

CHECKS OUTSTANDING NOT CHARGED TO ACCOUNT

No.	$	
TOTAL	$	

BEFORE YOU START

PLEASE BE SURE YOU HAVE ENTERED IN YOUR CHECKBOOK ALL AUTOMATIC TRANSACTIONS SHOWN ON THE FRONT OF YOUR STATEMENT.

YOU SHOULD HAVE ADDED IF ANY OCCURRED:

1. Loan advances.
2. Credit memos.
3. Other automatic deposits.

YOU SHOULD HAVE SUBTRACTED IF ANY OCCURRED:

1. Automatic loan payments.
2. Automatic savings transfers.
3. Service charges.
4. Debit memos.
5. Other automatic deductions and payments.

BANK BALANCE SHOWN
ON THIS STATEMENT $ _____

ADD

DEPOSITS NOT SHOWN
ON THIS STATEMENT
(IF ANY) $ _____

_____

_____

TOTAL $ _____

SUBTRACT

CHECKS OUTSTANDING $ _____

BALANCE $ _____

SHOULD AGREE WITH YOUR CHECKBOOK BALANCE AFTER DEDUCTING SERVICE CHARGES (IF ANY) SHOWN ON THIS STATEMENT.

Please examine immediately and report if incorrect. If no reply is received within 15 days, the account will be considered correct.

IN CASE OF ERRORS OR INQUIRIES ABOUT YOUR BILL

Send your inquiry in writing on a separate sheet so that the creditor receives it within 60 days after the bill was mailed to you. Your written inquiry must include:

1. Your name and account number;
2. A description of the error and why (to the extent you can explain) you believe it is an error; and
3. The dollar amount of the suspected error.

If you have authorized your creditor to automatically pay your bill from your checking or savings account, you can stop or reverse payment on any amount you think is wrong by mailing your notice so that the creditor receives it within 16 days after the bill was sent to you.

You remain obligated to pay the parts of your bill not in dispute, but you do not have to pay any amount in dispute during the time the creditor is resolving the dispute. During that same time, the creditor may not take any action to collect disputed amounts or report disputed amounts as delinquent.

This is a summary of your rights; a full statement of your rights and the creditor's responsibilities under the Federal Fair Credit Billing Act will be sent to you both upon request and in response to a billing error notice.

APPENDIX B
PROBLEM B-1

GENERAL JOURNAL

PAGE ___17___

	DATE		DESCRIPTION	POST. REF.	DEBIT	CREDIT	
1							1
2							2
3							3
4							4
5							5
6							6
7							7
8							8
9							9
10							10
11							11
12							12
13							13
14							14

PROBLEM B-2

GENERAL JOURNAL

PAGE ___46___

	DATE		DESCRIPTION	POST. REF.	DEBIT	CREDIT	
1							1
2							2
3							3
4							4
5							5
6							6
7							7
8							8
9							9
10							10
11							11
12							12
13							13
14							14
15							15
16							16
17							17
18							18

APPENDIX B
PROBLEM B-3

GENERAL JOURNAL

PAGE ___ *47*

	DATE		DESCRIPTION	POST. REF.	DEBIT	CREDIT	
1							1
2							2
3							3
4							4
5							5
6							6
7							7
8							8
9							9
10							10
11							11
12							12
13							13
14							14
15							15
16							16
17							17
18							18
19							19
20							20
21							21
22							22
23							23
24							24
25							25
26							26
27							27
28							28
29							29
30							30
31							31
32							32
33							33
34							34
35							35
36							36
37							37

9 | Payroll Accounting: Employee Earnings and Deductions

LEARNING OBJECTIVES

1. Calculate total earnings based on an hourly, piece-rate, or commission basis.
2. Determine deductions from tables of employees' income tax withholding.
3. Complete a payroll register.
4. Journalize the payroll entry from a payroll register.
5. Maintain employees' individual earnings records.

KEY TERMS

Calendar year
Employee
Employee's individual earnings record
Employee's Withholding Allowance
   Certificate (Form W-4)
Exemption
FICA taxes
Gross pay

Independent contractor
Medicare taxes
Net pay
Payroll bank account
Payroll register
Social Security taxes
Taxable earnings
Wage bracket table

STUDY GUIDE QUESTIONS

PART 1   True/False

For each of the following statements, circle T if the statement is true and F if the statement is false.

T   F   1. Social Security and Medicare taxes are paid by both the employer and the employee.

T   F   2. The difference between an employee's net pay and her take-home pay is the amount of her personal deductions.

T   F   3. Information for an employee's individual earnings record is taken directly from the general journal.

T   F   4. The payroll register is considered to be a book of original entry.

T   F   5. On a payroll register, an employee's net amount paid equals total earnings minus total individual deductions.

T   F   6. All employers should use a special payroll bank account.

T   F   7. Individual earnings records should be kept for salaried employees.

T   F   8. The basis for the payroll register is the payroll journal entry.

T   F   9. Employees are required by law to participate in the Social Security program provided by the FICA.

T   F   10. The fee paid by a company to a CPA for auditing its books is subject to income tax withholding.

PART 2 Completion—Language of Business

Complete each of the following statements by writing the appropriate word(s) in the spaces provided.

1. Total earnings for an employee are called the employee's _____.
2. A(n) _____ is one who works for compensation under the direction or control of an employer.
3. Another term having the same meaning as a withholding allowance is a(n) _____ _____.
4. Another term having the same meaning as take-home pay is _____.
5. Someone who is engaged for a definite job and who chooses his or her own means of doing the work is a(n) _____.
6. Each employee's personal payroll information for the year is listed in the _____ _____.

PART 3 Calculation of Earnings

Henderson Company pays its employees time-and-a-half for all hours worked in excess of forty per week. For the first week of October, determine the total earnings for each of the following employees.

Employee's Name	Hours Worked	Regular Hourly Rate	Total Earnings
A. L. Gonzales	42	$ 9.60	
L. A. Lamar	46	8.40	
C. W. Nelson	51	10.20	

PART 4 Payroll Entry

Using the column totals for the week ended March 14 as listed in the payroll register, give the entry in general journal form to record the payroll. Number the page 79.

Total Earnings	$93,640.00
Federal Income Tax Deduction	9,300.00
Social Security Tax Deduction	5,805.68
Medicare Tax Deduction	1,357.78
U.S. Savings Bonds Deduction	900.00
Union Dues Deduction	1,200.00
Medical Insurance Deduction	2,000.00
Net Amount	73,076.54
Sales Salary Expense	72,000.00
Office Salary Expense	21,640.00

DEMONSTRATION PROBLEM

Kelsey Company's payroll register reveals the following information concerning its two employees for the month ended July 31 of this year:

D. C. Garcia		T. C. Bennett	
Total earnings	$2,000.00	Total earnings	$1,800.00
Federal income tax withheld	400.00	Federal income tax withheld	360.00
Social Security tax withheld	124.00	Social Security tax withheld	111.60
Medicare tax withheld	29.00	Medicare tax withheld	26.10
Medical insurance withheld	129.00	Medical insurance withheld	125.00
Net amount (Ck. No. 6701)	1,318.00	Net amount (Ck. No. 6702)	1,177.30

The employees are paid by checks issued on the firm's regular bank account.

Record the payroll entry in a general journal.

SOLUTION

GENERAL JOURNAL

PAGE _____

DATE		DESCRIPTION	POST. REF.	DEBIT	CREDIT
19—					
July	31	Salary Expense		3 8 0 0 00	
		Employees' Income Tax Payable			7 6 0 00
		FICA Tax Payable			2 9 0 70
		Employees' Medical Insurance			
		Payable			2 5 4 00
		Cash			2 4 9 5 30
		Paid salaries for the month			
		(D.C. Garcia, $1,318, Ck.			
		No. 6701; T.C. Bennett,			
		$1,177.30, Ck. No. 6702).			

PROBLEM 9-1A or 9-1B

REGULAR PAY	OVERTIME PAY	GROSS PAY	NET PAY

PROBLEM 9-2A or 9-2B

(The payroll register for this problem is at the end of the book.)

GENERAL JOURNAL

PAGE _____

	DATE		DESCRIPTION	POST. REF.	DEBIT	CREDIT	
1							1
2							2
3							3
4							4
5							5
6							6
7							7
8							8
9							9
10							10
11							11
12							12
13							13
14							14
15							15
16							16
17							17
18							18
19							19
20							20
21							21
22							22
23							23
24							24
25							25
26							26
27							27
28							28
29							29
30							30
31							31
32							32
33							33
34							34
35							35
36							36
37							37

PROBLEM 9-3A or 9-3B

(The payroll register for this problem is at the end of the book.)

GENERAL JOURNAL   PAGE _____

	DATE	DESCRIPTION	POST. REF.	DEBIT	CREDIT	
1						1
2						2
3						3
4						4
5						5
6						6
7						7
8						8
9						9
10						10
11						11
12						12
13						13
14						14
15						15
16						16
17						17
18						18
19						19
20						20
21						21
22						22
23						23
24						24
25						25
26						26
27						27
28						28
29						29
30						30
31						31
32						32
33						33
34						34
35						35
36						36
37						37

PROBLEM 9-4A or 9-4B

(The payroll register for this problem is at the end of the book.)

GENERAL JOURNAL

PAGE _____

	DATE	DESCRIPTION	POST. REF.	DEBIT	CREDIT	
1						1
2						2
3						3
4						4
5						5
6						6
7						7
8						8
9						9
10						10
11						11
12						12
13						13
14						14
15						15
16						16
17						17
18						18
19						19
20						20
21						21
22						22
23						23
24						24
25						25
26						26
27						27
28						28
29						29
30						30
31						31
32						32
33						33
34						34
35						35
36						36
37						37

10 Payroll Accounting: Employer's Taxes, Payments, and Reports

LEARNING OBJECTIVES

1. Calculate the amount of payroll tax expense and journalize the related entry.
2. Journalize the entry for the deposit of employees' federal income taxes withheld and FICA taxes (both employees' withheld and employer's matching share).
3. Journalize the entries for the payment of employer's state and federal unemployment taxes.
4. Journalize the entry for the deposit of employees' state income taxes withheld.
5. Complete Employer's Quarterly Federal Tax Return, Form 941.
6. Prepare W-2 and W-3 forms and Form 940.
7. Calculate the premium for workers' compensation insurance, and prepare the entry for payment in advance.
8. Determine the amount of adjustment for workers' compensation insurance at the end of the year, and record the adjustment.

KEY TERMS

Eighth-of-a-month periods
Employer identification number
Federal unemployment tax
Form 940
Form 941
Form W-2

Form W-3
Payroll Tax Expense
Quarter
State unemployment tax
Workers' compensation insurance

STUDY GUIDE QUESTIONS

PART 1   True/False

For each of the following statements, circle T if the statement is true and F if the statement is false.

T   F   1. Companies must furnish their employees with W-2 forms by April 15.

T   F   2. The Payroll Tax Expense account handles the unemployment taxes as well as the employer's and employees' FICA taxes.

T   F   3. Form 941 is completed four times a year.

T   F   4. The times for making deposits of FICA taxes and employees' income taxes withheld depends strictly on the number of employees involved.

T   F   5. Form 940 is an annual tax return that relates to federal unemployment tax.

T   F   6. A premium for workers' compensation insurance is paid at the beginning of the year.

T   F   7. The state unemployment tax is determined by multiplying the net amount as shown in the payroll register by the state unemployment tax rate.

T   F   8. The federal unemployment tax is paid by the employer only.

T   F   9. If the Unemployment Taxable Earnings column of the payroll register is blank, this indicates that the employee has cumulative earnings for the calendar year of more than the maximum unemployment taxable income.

T   F   10. Form W-4 is submitted to the Internal Revenue Service along with copies of the employees' W-2 forms.

PART 2   Completion—Language of Business

Complete each of the following statements by writing the appropriate word(s) in the spaces provided.

1. The second _____ of the year consists of the months of April, May, and June.
2. _____ provides an employee with his or her total earnings and tax deductions.
3. Employers' reports submitted to the Internal Revenue Service are listed by the _____ _____ .
4. The _____ account is used to record the employer's matching portion of the FICA tax, the federal unemployment tax, and the state unemployment tax.
5. _____ is used to provide benefits for employees injured on the job.
6. Form _____ is submitted to the Social Security Administration accompanied by copies of W-2 forms.
7. _____ is the Employer's Quarterly Federal Tax Return.

PART 3   Completing Form W-2

Complete Form W-2 provided for June Clara Perkins. Perkins is employed by Barclay Company, 1620 Hampton Place, Boston, Massachusetts 02116. Barclay Company's federal employer identification number is 72-1162127, and its state identification number is 42-6916. The following information is taken from Perkins's Individual Earnings Record. Her address is 2219 Henderson Street, Boston, Mass., 02121. Her Social Security number is 561-24-5229. During the year, Perkins earned $34,218.42. Her withholdings were as follows: federal income tax, $3,716.22; state income tax, $1,780.04; Social Security tax withheld, $2,121.54; Medicare tax withheld, $496.67.

1 Control number 22222	For Official Use Only ▶ OMB No. 1545-0008	
2 Employer's name, address, and ZIP code	6 Statutory employee ☐ Deceased ☐ Pension plan ☐ Legal rep. ☐ 942 emp. ☐ Subtotal ☐ Deferred compensation ☐ Void ☐	
	7 Allocated tips	8 Advance EIC payment
	9 Federal income tax withheld	10 Wages, tips, other compensation
3 Employer's identification number	4 Employer's state I.D. number	11 Social security tax withheld	12 Social security wages
5 Employee's social security number		13 Social security tips	14 Medicare wages and tips
19a Employee's name (first, middle, last)	15 Medicare tax withheld	16 Nonqualified plans
	17 See Instrs. for Form W-2	18 Other
19b Employee's address and ZIP code		
20	21	22 Dependent care benefits	23 Benefits included in Box 10
24 State income tax	25 State wages, tips, etc.	26 Name of state	27 Local income tax	28 Local wages, tips, etc.	29 Name of locality

Copy A For Social Security Administration   Department of the Treasury—Internal Revenue Service

Form W-2 Wage and Tax Statement

For Paperwork Reduction Act Notice, see separate instructions.

PART 4 Completing Form 940

Complete Form 940 (on next page) as of January 30 for the preceding calendar year for C. N. Millard, owner of Millard and Company, 820 Starbuck Road, Nelson, Wyoming 82894. Total earnings for employees are as follows: Files, $32,140; Gray, $39,920; Lang, $21,640. The federal unemployment tax is .8 percent of the first $7,000 paid to each employee during the calendar year. The state unemployment tax is 5.4 percent of the first $7,000 paid to each employee during the year. The state reporting number is 367-514. The state tax has been paid. Millard and Company is required to pay state unemployment insurance to the state of Wyoming only. The employer's federal tax number is 29-5229364. The federal tax liability for the first quarter is $20,170, and the liability for the second quarter is $830.

A summary of the Federal Unemployment Tax Payable account, by quarterly periods, is shown below. No liabilities for federal and state unemployment tax were incurred during the third and fourth quarters.

FEDERAL UNEMPLOYMENT TAX PAYABLE

DATE	ITEM	DEBIT	CREDIT	BALANCE DEBIT	BALANCE CREDIT
3/31	First quarter		1 6 1 36		1 6 1 36
4/12	Federal tax deposit	1 6 1 36			
6/30	Second quarter		6 64		6 64

Form 940

Department of the Treasury
Internal Revenue Service

Employer's Annual Federal Unemployment (FUTA) Tax Return

▶ For Paperwork Reduction Act Notice, see page 2.

OMB No. 1545-0028

T	
FF	
FD	
FP	
I	
T	

If Incorrect, make any necessary change. ▶

Name (as distinguished from trade name)

Trade name, if any

Address and ZIP code

Calendar year

Employer identification number

—

A Did you pay all required contributions to state unemployment funds by the due date of Form 940? (See instructions if none required.) . . . . ☐ Yes ☐ No

If you checked the "Yes" box, enter the amount of contributions paid to state unemployment funds . . . . ▶ $ _____

B Are you required to pay contributions to only one state? . . . . ☐ Yes ☐ No

If you checked the "Yes" box: (1) Enter the name of the state where you are required to pay contributions . . . ▶ _____

(2) Enter your state reporting number(s) as shown on state unemployment tax return. ▶ _____

C If any part of wages taxable for FUTA tax is exempt from state unemployment tax, check the box. (See the Specific Instructions on page 4.) . . . . ☐

Note: If you checked the "Yes" boxes in both questions A and B and did not check the box in C above, you may be able to use Form 940-EZ.

If you will not have to file returns in the future, write "Final" here (see general instruction "Who Must File") and sign the return. ▶

Part I Computation of Taxable Wages (to be completed by all taxpayers)

1	Total payments (including exempt payments) during the calendar year for services of employees	1	
2	Exempt payments. (Explain each exemption shown, attaching additional sheets if necessary.) ▶ _____	Amount paid	
		2	
3	Payments for services of more than $7,000. Enter only the excess over the first $7,000 paid to individual employees not including exempt amounts shown on line 2. Do not use the state wage limitation.	3	
4	Total exempt payments (add lines 2 and 3)	4	
5	**Total taxable wages** (subtract line 4 from line 1). (If any part is exempt from state contributions, see instructions.) ▶	5	

Part II Tax Due or Refund (Complete if you checked the "Yes" boxes in both questions A and B and did not check the box in C above.)

1	**Total FUTA tax.** Multiply the wages in Part I, line 5, by .008 and enter here	1	
2	Total FUTA tax deposited for the year, including any overpayment applied from a prior year (from your records)	2	
3	**Balance due** (subtract line 2 from line 1). This should be $100 or less. Pay to IRS . . . . . ▶	3	
4	**Overpayment** (subtract line 1 from line 2). Check if it is to be: ☐ Applied to next return, or ☐ Refunded ▶	4	

Part III Tax Due or Refund (Complete if you checked the "No" box in either question A or B or you checked the box in C above. Also complete Part V.)

1	Gross FUTA tax. Multiply the wages in Part I, line 5, by .062	1	
2	Maximum credit. Multiply the wages in Part I, line 5, by .054	2	
3	**Credit allowable:** Enter the smaller of the amount in Part V, line 11, or Part III, line 2 . .	3	
4	**Total FUTA tax** (subtract line 3 from line 1)	4	
5	Total FUTA tax deposited for the year, including any overpayment applied from a prior year (from your records)	5	
6	**Balance due** (subtract line 5 from line 4). This should be $100 or less. Pay to IRS . . . . . ▶	6	
7	**Overpayment** (subtract line 4 from line 5). Check if it is to be: ☐ Applied to next return, or ☐ Refunded ▶	7	

Part IV Record of Quarterly Federal Tax Liability for Unemployment Tax (Do not include state liability.)

Quarter	First	Second	Third	Fourth	Total for Year
Liability for quarter					

Part V Computation of Tentative Credit (Complete if you checked the "No" box in either question A or B or you checked the box in C above—see instructions.)

Name of state	State reporting number(s) as shown on employer's state contribution returns	Taxable payroll (as defined in state act)	State experience rate period		State experience rate	Contributions if rate had been 5.4% (col. 3 x .054)	Contributions payable at experience rate (col. 3 x col. 5)	Additional credit (col. 6 minus col.7) If 0 or less, enter 0.	Contributions actually paid to the state
			From—	To—					
1	**2**	**3**	**4**		**5**	**6**	**7**	**8**	**9**

10 Totals . . . . . ▶

11 Total tentative credit (add line 10, columns 8 and 9 only—see instructions for limitations) . . . . ▶

Under penalties of perjury, I declare that I have examined this return, including accompanying schedules and statements, and to the best of my knowledge and belief, it is true, correct, and complete, and that no part of any payment made to a state unemployment fund claimed as a credit was or is to be deducted from the payments to employees.

Signature ▶

Title (Owner, etc.) ▶

Date ▶

Form **940**

DEMONSTRATION PROBLEM

The totals of the payroll register (page 73) for City-Wide Moving are given below. Assume the employment taxes are as follows:

State unemployment, 5.4 percent
Federal unemployment, .8 percent
Social Security, 6.2 percent
Medicare, 1.45 percent

Total Earnings	$86,000
State Unemployment Taxable Earnings	18,000
Federal Unemployment Taxable Earnings	18,000
Social Security Taxable Earnings	84,000
Medicare Taxable Earnings	86,000
Federal Income Tax Deduction	9,800
Social Security tax deduction	5,208
Medicare tax deduction	1,247
Union Dues Deduction	1,560
Medical Insurance Deduction	4,250
Total Deductions	22,065
Net Pay	63,935

Instructions

Journalize the following entries:

a. To record the payroll, assuming the use of a payroll bank account
b. To record the payroll tax expense
c. To record payment to the employees
d. To record the deposit of federal taxes that will be reported on the Employer's Quarterly Federal Tax Return (Form 941): employees' income taxes withheld, employees' FICA taxes withheld, and employer's share of FICA tax.
e. To record payment of state unemployment insurance that will be reported on the state unemployment insurance tax form.
f. To record the deposit of federal unemployment insurance that will be reported on the Employer's Annual Federal Unemployment Tax Return (Form 940)
g. To record payment of employees' union dues withheld
h. To record payment of employees' medical insurance withheld

SOLUTION

GENERAL JOURNAL

DATE		DESCRIPTION	POST. REF.	DEBIT		CREDIT	
	a.	Wages Expense		86 0 0 0 00			
		Employees' Federal Income Tax					
		Payable				9 8 0 0 00	
		FICA Tax Payable				6 4 5 5 00	
		Employees' Union Dues Payable				1 5 6 0 00	
		Employees' Medical Insurance					
		Payable				4 2 5 0 00	
		Wages Payable				63 9 3 5 00	
		To record wages as listed in					
		the payroll register, page 73.					
	b.	Payroll Tax Expense		7 5 7 1 00			
		FICA Tax Payable				6 4 5 5 00	
		State Unemployment Tax Payable				9 7 2 00	
		Federal Unemployment Tax					
		Payable				1 4 4 00	
		To record employer's share of					
		FICA tax and federal and state					
		unemployment taxes. (FICA					
		tax = Social Security tax +					
		Medicare tax: Social Security					
		tax = $84,000 × .062 =					
		$5,208					
		Medicare tax = $86,000 ×					
		.0145 = $1,247					
		FICA tax = $5,208 +					
		$1,247 = $6,455.)					
	c.	Wages Payable		63 9 3 5 00			
		Cash				63 9 3 5 00	
		To record payment of employees,					
		by issuing one check payable to					
		payroll bank account.					

DATE	DESCRIPTION	POST. REF.	DEBIT	CREDIT
d.	Employees' Income Tax Payable		9 8 0 0 00	
	FICA Tax Payable		12 9 1 0 00	
	Cash			22 7 1 0 00
	Issued check to record deposit			
	of federal taxes.			
e.	State Unemployment Tax Payable		9 7 2 00	
	Cash			9 7 2 00
	To record payment of state			
	unemployment tax.			
f.	Federal Unemployment Tax Payable		1 4 4 00	
	Cash			1 4 4 00
	To record deposit of federal			
	unemployment insurance.			
g.	Employees' Union Dues Payable		1 5 6 0 00	
	Cash			1 5 6 0 00
	To record payment of employees'			
	union dues withheld.			
h.	Employees' Medical Insurance			
	Payable		4 2 5 0 00	
	Cash			4 2 5 0 00
	To record payment of employees'			
	medical insurance premiums			
	withheld.			

PROBLEM 10-1A or 10-1B

GENERAL JOURNAL

	DATE	DESCRIPTION	POST. REF.	DEBIT	CREDIT	
1						1
2						2
3						3
4						4
5						5
6						6
7						7
8						8
9						9
10						10
11						11
12						12
13						13
14						14
15						15
16						16
17						17
18						18
19						19
20						20
21						21
22						22
23						23
24						24
25						25
26						26
27						27
28						28
29						29
30						30
31						31
32						32
33						33
34						34
35						35
36						36
37						37

PROBLEM 10-2A or 10-2B

(The payroll register for this problem is at the end of the book.)

GENERAL JOURNAL

PAGE _____

	DATE	DESCRIPTION	POST. REF.	DEBIT	CREDIT	
1						1
2						2
3						3
4						4
5						5
6						6
7						7
8						8
9						9
10						10
11						11
12						12
13						13
14						14
15						15
16						16
17						17
18						18
19						19
20						20
21						21
22						22
23						23
24						24
25						25
26						26
27						27
28						28
29						29
30						30
31						31
32						32
33						33
34						34
35						35
36						36
37						37

PROBLEM 10-3A or 10-3B

Form **941**

Department of the Treasury
Internal Revenue Service   4141

Employer's Quarterly Federal Tax Return

▶ See Circular E for more information concerning employment tax returns.

Please type or print.

Your name, address, employer identification number, and calendar quarter of return. (If not correct, please change.)

▶

Name (as distinguished from trade name)   Date quarter ended

Trade name, if any   Employer identification number

Address and ZIP code

OMB No. 1545-0029

T
FF
FD
FP
I
T

If address is different from prior return, check here ▶ ☐

IRS Use

1 1 1 1 1 1 1 1 1 1 1   2   3 3 3 3 3 3   4 4 4

5 5 5   6   7   8 8 8 8 8   9 9 9   10 10 10 10 10 10 10 10 10 10

If you do not have to file returns in the future, check here . . . ▶ ☐   Date final wages paid . . . ▶ _____

If you are a seasonal employer, see **Seasonal employers** on page 2 and check here . ▶ ☐

1a Number of employees (except household) employed in the pay period that includes March 12th . ▶	**1a**	
b If you are a subsidiary corporation AND your parent corporation files a consolidated Form 1120, enter parent corporation employer identification number (EIN) . . ▶ **1b** –		
2 Total wages and tips subject to withholding, plus other compensation . . . . ▶	**2**	
3 Total income tax withheld from wages, tips, pensions, annuities, sick pay, gambling, etc. . . ▶	**3**	
4 Adjustment of withheld income tax for preceding quarters of calendar year (see instructions) . .	**4**	
5 Adjusted total of income tax withheld (line 3 as adjusted by line 4—see instructions) . .	**5**	
6a Taxable social security wages **(Complete line 7)** $ _____ × 12.4% (.124) =	**6a**	
b Taxable social security tips $ _____ × 12.4% (.124) =	**6b**	
7 Taxable Medicare wages and tips . . . . . $ _____ × 2.9% (.029) =	**7**	
8 Total social security and Medicare taxes (add lines 6a, 6b, and 7)	**8**	
9 Adjustment of social security and Medicare taxes (see instructions for required explanation) . .	**9**	
10 Adjusted total of social security and Medicare taxes (line 8 as adjusted by line 9—see instructions) ▶	**10**	
11 Backup withholding (see instructions)	**11**	
12 Adjustment of backup withholding tax for preceding quarters of calendar year. . . . . ▶	**12**	
13 Adjusted total of backup withholding (line 11 as adjusted by line 12)	**13**	
14 **Total taxes** (add lines 5, 10, and 13)	**14**	
15 Advance earned income credit (EIC) payments made to employees, if any . . . . . . ▶	**15**	
16 Net taxes (subtract line 15 from line 14). **This should equal line IV below** (plus line IV of Schedule A (Form 941) if you have treated backup withholding as a separate liability)	**16**	
17 **Total deposits for quarter,** including overpayment applied from a prior quarter, from your records. ▶	**17**	
18 **Balance due** (subtract line 17 from line 16). This should be less than $500. Pay to IRS . . . . ▶	**18**	

19 Overpayment, if line 17 is more than line 16, enter here ▶ $ _____ and check if to be:
☐ Applied to next return   **OR**   ☐ Refunded.

Record of Federal Tax Liability (You must complete if line 16 is $500 or more and Schedule B is not attached.) See instructions before checking these boxes.
Check only if you made deposits using the 95% rule ▶ ☐   Check only if you are a first time 3-banking-day depositor. . . ▶ ☐

Show tax liability here, **not deposits.** IRS gets deposit data from FTD coupons.

Date wages paid		First month of quarter		Second month of quarter		Third month of quarter
1st through 3rd	A		I		Q	
4th through 7th	B		J		R	
8th through 11th	C		K		S	
12th through 15th	D		L		T	
16th through 19th	E		M		U	
20th through 22nd	F		N		V	
23rd through 25th	G		O		W	
26th through the last	H		P		X	
Total liability for month	I		II		III	

(Do NOT Show Federal Tax Deposits Here)

▶ **IV** Total for quarter (add lines **I**, **II**, and **III**). **This should equal line 16 above** . . . . . . ▶

Sign Here

Under penalties of perjury, I declare that I have examined this return, including accompanying schedules and statements, and to the best of my knowledge and belief, it is true, correct, and complete.

Signature ▶ _____   Print Your Name and Title ▶ _____   Date ▶ _____

For Paperwork Reduction Act Notice, see page 2.

PROBLEM 10-4A or 10-4B

GENERAL JOURNAL

PAGE _____

	DATE		DESCRIPTION	POST. REF.	DEBIT	CREDIT	
1							1
2							2
3							3
4							4
5							5
6							6
7							7
8							8
9							9
10							10
11							11
12							12
13							13
14							14
15							15
16							16
17							17
18							18
19							19
20							20
21							21
22							22
23							23
24							24
25							25
26							26
27							27
28							28
29							29
30							30
31							31
32							32
33							33
34							34
35							35
36							36
37							37

PROBLEM 10-4A or 10-4B (concluded)

GENERAL JOURNAL

PAGE _____

	DATE	DESCRIPTION	POST. REF.	DEBIT	CREDIT	
1						1
2						2
3						3
4						4
5						5
6						6
7						7
8						8
9						9
10						10
11						11
12						12
13						13
14						14
15						15
16						16
17						17
18						18
19						19
20						20
21						21
22						22
23						23
24						24
25						25
26						26
27						27
28						28
29						29
30						30
31						31
32						32
33						33
34						34
35						35
36						36
37						37

Accounting for Merchandise: Sales

LEARNING OBJECTIVES

1. Describe the specific accounts used by a merchandising firm.
2. Record transactions in sales journals.
3. Post from sales journals to an accounts receivable ledger and a general ledger.
4. Prepare a schedule of accounts receivable.
5. Record and post to the ledger accounts, sales returns and allowances, including credit memorandums and returns involving sales tax.
6. Locate errors.
7. Post directly from sales invoices to an accounts receivable ledger and journalize and post a summarizing entry in the general journal.

KEY TERMS

Accounts receivable ledger
Controlling account
Credit memorandum
Freight In
Merchandise inventory
Purchases
Purchases Discount
Purchases Returns and Allowances

Sales
Sales Discount
Sales journal
Sales Returns and Allowances
Sales tax
Special journals
Subsidiary ledger
Summarizing entry

STUDY GUIDE QUESTIONS

PART 1   True/False

For each of the following statements, circle T if the statement is true and F if the statement is false.

T   F   1. Posting from the sales journal to the Accounts Receivable account in the general ledger takes place at the end of the month.

T   F   2. The sales journal is used to record all sales.

T   F   3. Businesses that keep their books manually list customer accounts in alphabetical order in their accounts receivable ledger.

T   F   4. Increases in Sales Returns and Allowances are recorded on the credit side.

T   F   5. Check marks in the Posting Reference column of the sales journal indicate that the amounts are not to be posted.

T   F   6. At the end of the month, after all posting is completed, the total of the schedule of accounts receivable should equal the balance of the Sales account in the general ledger.

T   F   7. The accounts receivable ledger contains a separate account for each sale.

T   F   8. In posting directly from a sales invoice, the invoice number rather than the journal page number is recorded in the Posting Reference columns of customer accounts in the accounts receivable ledger.

T   F   9. When using a sales journal, you do not have to post to any accounts in the general ledger.

T   F   10. The schedule of accounts receivable lists the balances of all the charge customer accounts at the end of the month.

PART 2 Completion—Language of Business

Complete each of the following statements by writing the appropriate word(s) in the spaces provided.

1. The book of original entry used to record sales of merchandise on account is called a(n) _____ .

2. A stock of ready-made goods that a company buys and intends to sell at a profit is called _____ .

3. Books of original entry used to record separate types of transactions are referred to as _____ .

4. The Accounts Receivable account in the general ledger is called a(n) _____ .

5. The accounts receivable ledger may be called a special ledger or a(n) _____ .

6. A document issued by the seller to a customer allowing a reduction from the price at which the goods were originally sold is called a(n) _____ .

7. The entry made at the end of the month when amounts are posted directly from sales invoices is referred to as the _____ .

PART 3 Posting

Post the following sales journal to the accounts in the general ledger.

SALES JOURNAL
PAGE _____ 26 _____

DATE		INV. NO.	CUSTOMER'S NAME	POST. REF.	ACCOUNTS RECEIVABLE DEBIT	SALES TAX PAYABLE CREDIT	SALES CREDIT
19—							
June	1	32	Calvin Parsons		1 4 5 60	5 60	1 4 0 00
	30	171	Clara Lambert		1 6 1 41	6 21	1 5 5 20
	30				3 1 6 8 07	1 2 1 85	3 0 4 6 22

GENERAL LEDGER

ACCOUNT _Accounts Receivable_ _____ ACCOUNT NO. _____ 113 _____

DATE	ITEM	POST. REF.	DEBIT	CREDIT	BALANCE	
					DEBIT	CREDIT

ACCOUNT **Sales Tax Payable**   ACCOUNT NO. 214

DATE	ITEM	POST. REF.	DEBIT	CREDIT	BALANCE DEBIT	BALANCE CREDIT

ACCOUNT **Sales**   ACCOUNT NO. 411

DATE	ITEM	POST. REF.	DEBIT	CREDIT	BALANCE DEBIT	BALANCE CREDIT

DEMONSTRATION PROBLEM

The following selected transactions were completed by the Adams Company:

Sept. 16 Sold merchandise on account to the Foster Company, sales invoice no. 1032, $3,742.
20 Sold merchandise on account to the King Company, sales invoice no. 1033, $8,950.
25 As an accommodation, sold supplies on account (at cost) to Zimmer Company, $173.
27 King Company returned $982 of merchandise relating to sales invoice no. 1033; Adams Company issued credit memo no. 131.

Instructions

1. Record the transactions in either the sales journal or the general journal, as appropriate.
2. Immediately after recording each transaction, post to the accounts receivable ledger.
3. Post the entries from the general journal and the sales journal to the general ledger.
4. Prepare a schedule of accounts receivable.
5. Compare the total of the schedule of accounts receivable with the September 30 balance of the Accounts Receivable controlling account.

SOLUTION

SALES JOURNAL   PAGE 134

DATE		INV. NO.	CUSTOMER'S NAME	POST. REF.	ACCOUNTS RECEIVABLE DR., SALES CR.
19—					
Sept.	16	1032	Foster Company	√	3 7 4 2 00
	20	1033	King Company	√	8 9 5 0 00
	30				12 6 9 2 00
					(113) (411)

DATE		DESCRIPTION	POST. REF.	DEBIT	CREDIT
19—					
Sept.	25	Accounts Receivable, Zimmer Company	113/✓	1 7 3 00	
		Supplies	115		1 7 3 00
		Sold supplies at cost.			
	27	Sales Returns and Allowances	412	9 8 2 00	
		Accounts Receivable, King Company	113/✓		9 8 2 00
		Credit memo no. 131 relating to invoice			
		no. 1033.			

GENERAL LEDGER

ACCOUNT _Accounts Receivable_   ACCOUNT NO. _113_

DATE		ITEM	POST. REF.	DEBIT	CREDIT	BALANCE DEBIT	BALANCE CREDIT
19—							
Sept.	1	Balance	✓			5 3 9 0 00	
	25		J159	1 7 3 00		5 5 6 3 00	
	27		J159		9 8 2 00	4 5 8 1 00	
	30		S134	12 6 9 2 00		17 2 7 3 00	

ACCOUNT _Supplies_   ACCOUNT NO. _115_

DATE		ITEM	POST. REF.	DEBIT	CREDIT	BALANCE DEBIT	BALANCE CREDIT
19—							
Sept.	1	Balance	✓			1 5 5 0 00	
	25		J159		1 7 3 00	1 3 7 7 00	

ACCOUNT _Sales_   ACCOUNT NO. _411_

DATE		ITEM	POST. REF.	DEBIT	CREDIT	BALANCE DEBIT	BALANCE CREDIT
19—							
Sept.	1	Balance	✓				51 5 9 7 00
	30		S134		12 6 9 2 00		64 2 8 9 00

ACCOUNT _Sales Returns and Allowances_   ACCOUNT NO. _412_

DATE		ITEM	POST. REF.	DEBIT	CREDIT	BALANCE DEBIT	BALANCE CREDIT
19—							
Sept.	1	Balance	✓			2 7 7 7 00	
	27		J159	9 8 2 00		3 7 5 9 00	

NAME   *Foster Company*

ADDRESS   *330 Wexler Road, S.W.*

Atlanta, GA 30305

DATE		ITEM	POST. REF.	DEBIT	CREDIT	BALANCE
19—						
Sept.	1	Balance	✓			5 3 9 0 00
	16		S134	3 7 4 2 00		9 1 3 2 00

NAME   *King Company*

ADDRESS   *1450 Myron Avenue, S.W.*

Atlanta, GA 30307

DATE		ITEM	POST. REF.	DEBIT	CREDIT	BALANCE
19—						
Sept.	20		S134	8 9 5 0 00		8 9 5 0 00
	27		J159		9 8 2 00	7 9 6 8 00

NAME   *Zimmer Company*

ADDRESS   *1226 Euclid Avenue, S.W.*

Atlanta, GA 30309

DATE		ITEM	POST. REF.	DEBIT	CREDIT	BALANCE
19—						
Sept.	25		J159	1 7 3 00		1 7 3 00

Adams Company

Schedule of Accounts Receivable

September 30, 19—

Foster Company	$9 1 3 2 00
King Company	7 9 6 8 00
Zimmer Company	1 7 3 00
	$17 2 7 3 00

PROBLEM 11-1A or 11-1B

SALES JOURNAL

PAGE __41__

	DATE	INV. NO.	CUSTOMER'S NAME	POST. REF.	ACCOUNTS RECEIVABLE DR., SALES CR.	
1						1
2						2
3						3
4						4
5						5
6						6
7						7
8						8
9						9
10						10
11						11
12						12

GENERAL JOURNAL

PAGE __69__

	DATE	DESCRIPTION	POST. REF.	DEBIT	CREDIT	
1						1
2						2
3						3
4						4
5						5
6						6
7						7
8						8
9						9
10						10
11						11
12						12
13						13
14						14
15						15

PROBLEM 11-1A or 11-1B (continued)

GENERAL LEDGER

ACCOUNT **Accounts Receivable**   ACCOUNT NO. _113_

DATE	ITEM	POST. REF.	DEBIT	CREDIT	BALANCE DEBIT	BALANCE CREDIT
19—						
Sept. 1	Balance	✓			5 3 0 00	

ACCOUNT **Sales**   ACCOUNT NO. _411_

DATE	ITEM	POST. REF.	DEBIT	CREDIT	BALANCE DEBIT	BALANCE CREDIT
19—						
Sept. 1	Balance	✓				6 5 3 0 00

ACCOUNT **Sales Returns and Allowances**   ACCOUNT NO. _412_

DATE	ITEM	POST. REF.	DEBIT	CREDIT	BALANCE DEBIT	BALANCE CREDIT
19—						
Sept. 1	Balance	✓			3 8 9 00	

ACCOUNTS RECEIVABLE LEDGER

NAME **Allied Office Products**

ADDRESS **120 West Michaels St.**

Miami, FL 33197

DATE	ITEM	POST. REF.	DEBIT	CREDIT	BALANCE

PROBLEM 11-1A or 11-1B (concluded)

NAME _Best Supplies, Inc._
ADDRESS _1626 East Byron St._
Miami, FL 33184

DATE	ITEM	POST. REF.	DEBIT	CREDIT	BALANCE

NAME _Sheldon and Turner_
ADDRESS _2660 South Scott Ave._
Miami, FL 33192

DATE	ITEM	POST. REF.	DEBIT	CREDIT	BALANCE
19—					
Sept. 1	Balance	✓			5 3 0 00

NAME _Thomas Office Machines_
ADDRESS _1740 West Lowry St._
Miami, FL 33197

DATE	ITEM	POST. REF.	DEBIT	CREDIT	BALANCE

PROBLEM 11-2A or 11-2B

SALES JOURNAL

	DATE	INV. NO.	CUSTOMER'S NAME	POST. REF.	ACCOUNTS RECEIVABLE DR., SALES CR.	
1						1
2						2
3						3
4						4
5						5
6						6
7						7
8						8
9						9
10						10
11						11

GENERAL JOURNAL

	DATE	DESCRIPTION	POST. REF.	DEBIT	CREDIT	
1						1
2						2
3						3
4						4
5						5
6						6
7						7
8						8
9						9
10						10
11						11
12						12
13						13
14						14

PROBLEM 11-2A or 11-2B (continued)

GENERAL LEDGER

ACCOUNT _Accounts Receivable_ _____ ACCOUNT NO. _113_

DATE		ITEM	POST. REF.	DEBIT	CREDIT	BALANCE	
						DEBIT	CREDIT
19—							
June	1	Balance	✓			1 2 2 2 42	

ACCOUNT _Sales_ _____ ACCOUNT NO. _411_

DATE		ITEM	POST. REF.	DEBIT	CREDIT	BALANCE	
						DEBIT	CREDIT
19—							
June	1	Balance	✓				12 4 7 5 21

ACCOUNT _Sales Returns and Allowances_ _____ ACCOUNT NO. _412_

DATE		ITEM	POST. REF.	DEBIT	CREDIT	BALANCE	
						DEBIT	CREDIT
19—							
June	1	Balance	✓			4 2 6 13	

ACCOUNTS RECEIVABLE LEDGER

NAME _Beckon and Smith_

ADDRESS _640 W. Brighton St._
Chicago, IL 60692

DATE		ITEM	POST. REF.	DEBIT	CREDIT	BALANCE
19—						
June	1	Balance	✓			9 5 7 90

PROBLEM 11-2A or 11-2B (continued)

NAME _Henley Company_

ADDRESS _2132 W. Cato Blvd._

Chicago, IL 60694

DATE	ITEM	POST. REF.	DEBIT	CREDIT	BALANCE

NAME _Hoffmeier Company_

ADDRESS _2743 N. Danton Ave._

Chicago, IL 60692

DATE	ITEM	POST. REF.	DEBIT	CREDIT	BALANCE

NAME _S. N. King Company_

ADDRESS _3791 N. Eton Ave._

Chicago, IL 60691

DATE		ITEM	POST. REF.	DEBIT	CREDIT	BALANCE
19—						
June	1	Balance	✓			2 6 4 52

NAME _Lee Hardware_

ADDRESS _7216 E. Burrard St._

Chicago, IL 60695

DATE	ITEM	POST. REF.	DEBIT	CREDIT	BALANCE

PROBLEM 11-2A or 11-2B (concluded)

NAME *Mayer Construction*
ADDRESS *762 N. Sissler Ave.*
Chicago, IL 60693

DATE		ITEM	POST. REF.	DEBIT	CREDIT	BALANCE

PROBLEM 11-3A or 11-3B

SALES JOURNAL

PAGE ___34___

	DATE	INV. NO.	CUSTOMER'S NAME	POST. REF.	ACCOUNTS RECEIVABLE DEBIT	SALES TAX PAYABLE CREDIT	SALES CREDIT	
1								1
2								2
3								3
4								4
5								5
6								6
7								7
8								8
9								9
10								10
11								11

GENERAL JOURNAL

PAGE ___79___

	DATE	DESCRIPTION	POST. REF.	DEBIT	CREDIT	
1						1
2						2
3						3
4						4
5						5
6						6
7						7
8						8
9						9
10						10
11						11
12						12
13						13
14						14
15						15
16						16

PROBLEM 11-3A or 11-3B (continued)

GENERAL LEDGER

ACCOUNT *Accounts Receivable* _____ ACCOUNT NO. __113__

DATE		ITEM	POST. REF.	DEBIT	CREDIT	BALANCE	
						DEBIT	CREDIT
19—							
May	1	Balance	✓			1 2 8 25	

ACCOUNT *Sales Tax Payable* _____ ACCOUNT NO. __214__

DATE		ITEM	POST. REF.	DEBIT	CREDIT	BALANCE	
						DEBIT	CREDIT
19–							
May	1	Balance	✓				8 3 59

ACCOUNT *Sales* _____ ACCOUNT NO. __411__

DATE	ITEM	POST. REF.	DEBIT	CREDIT	BALANCE	
					DEBIT	CREDIT

ACCOUNT *Sales Returns and Allowances* _____ ACCOUNT NO. __412__

DATE	ITEM	POST. REF.	DEBIT	CREDIT	BALANCE	
					DEBIT	CREDIT

PROBLEM 11-3A or 11-3B (continued)

ACCOUNTS RECEIVABLE LEDGER

NAME _Clara's Boutique_

ADDRESS _6541 Bingham Rd. S._
Baltimore, MD 21294

DATE		ITEM	POST. REF.	DEBIT	CREDIT	BALANCE
19—						
May	1	Balance	✓			4 3 25

NAME _R. W. Cook_

ADDRESS _4839 Harrow St. W._
Baltimore, MD 21292

DATE		ITEM	POST. REF.	DEBIT	CREDIT	BALANCE

NAME _First Community Church_

ADDRESS _483 Stevens Ave. S._
Baltimore, MD 21297

DATE		ITEM	POST. REF.	DEBIT	CREDIT	BALANCE
19—						
May	1	Balance	✓			6 5 50

NAME _C. Lambert_

ADDRESS _977 Second Ave. S._
Baltimore, MD 21297

DATE		ITEM	POST. REF.	DEBIT	CREDIT	BALANCE

PROBLEM 11-3A or 11-3B (concluded)

NAME _L.C. Scheib_
ADDRESS _4169 Ellsworth Blvd., E._
Baltimore, MD 21295

DATE		ITEM	POST. REF.	DEBIT	CREDIT	BALANCE
19—						
May	1	Balance	√			1 9 50

NAME _Winnie's Child Care_
ADDRESS _980 Dempsey Rd. W._
Baltimore, MD 21296

DATE	ITEM	POST. REF.	DEBIT	CREDIT	BALANCE

PROBLEM 11-4A or 11-4B

GENERAL JOURNAL

	DATE	DESCRIPTION	POST. REF.	DEBIT	CREDIT	
1						1
2						2
3						3
4						4
5						5
6						6

GENERAL LEDGER

ACCOUNT *Accounts Receivable*   ACCOUNT NO. *113*

DATE		ITEM	POST. REF.	DEBIT	CREDIT	BALANCE DEBIT	BALANCE CREDIT
19—							
Oct.	1	Balance	√			882 00	

ACCOUNT *Sales*   ACCOUNT NO. *411*

DATE		ITEM	POST. REF.	DEBIT	CREDIT	BALANCE DEBIT	BALANCE CREDIT
19—							
Oct.	1	Balance	√				35108 00

ACCOUNTS RECEIVABLE LEDGER

NAME *Barden and Howell*

ADDRESS *482 E. Walsh Rd.*
Detroit, MI 48295

DATE		ITEM	POST. REF.	DEBIT	CREDIT	BALANCE
19—						
Oct.	1	Balance	√			275 00

PROBLEM 11-4A or 11-4B (continued)

NAME _Chadwick and Martin_

ADDRESS _6141 W. Regal Blvd._

Detroit, MI 48294

DATE		ITEM	POST. REF.	DEBIT	CREDIT	BALANCE

NAME _Chase and Company_

ADDRESS _549 S. Gunter Ave._

Detroit, MI 48295

DATE		ITEM	POST. REF.	DEBIT	CREDIT	BALANCE

NAME _M. M. Davis_

ADDRESS _2867 W. Hafer Rd._

Detroit, MI 48293

DATE		ITEM	POST. REF.	DEBIT	CREDIT	BALANCE
19—						
Oct.	1	Balance	✓			3 9 5 00

NAME _Gifford Specialty Company_

ADDRESS _964 S. Pierce Ave._

Detroit, MI 48295

DATE		ITEM	POST. REF.	DEBIT	CREDIT	BALANCE

PROBLEM 11-4A or 11-4B (concluded)

NAME _Goff Athletic Supply_

ADDRESS _3820 W. Verner St._

Detroit, MI 48293

DATE		ITEM	POST. REF.	DEBIT	CREDIT	BALANCE
19—						
Oct.	1	Balance	✓			2 1 2 00

NAME _S. L. Singer Company_

ADDRESS _1320 E. Trager St._

Detroit, MI 48294

DATE		ITEM	POST. REF.	DEBIT	CREDIT	BALANCE

Accounting for Merchandise: Purchases

LEARNING OBJECTIVES

1. Record transactions in a three-column purchases journal.
2. Post from a three-column purchases journal to an accounts payable ledger and a general ledger.
3. Record transactions involving purchases returns and allowances in a general journal.
4. Prepare a schedule of accounts payable.
5. Record transactions in a multicolumn purchases journal.
6. Post from a multicolumn purchases journal to an accounts payable ledger and a general ledger.
7. Post directly from purchase invoices to an accounts payable ledger and journalize and post a summarizing entry in the general journal.

KEY TERMS

Credit memorandum
Crossfooting
FOB destination
FOB shipping point
Freight In
Internal control

Invoice
Purchase order
Purchase requisition
Purchases discount
Purchases journal
Purchases Returns and Allowances

STUDY GUIDE QUESTIONS

PART 1   True/False

For each of the following statements, circle T if the statement is true and F if the statement is false:

T   F   1. The purchase requisition is sent to the supplier.

T   F   2. The Purchases account is used to record the buying of merchandise only.

T   F   3. Increases in the Purchases Returns and Allowances account are recorded on the debit side.

T   F   4. If the freight charges are FOB shipping point, the buyer pays the transportation charges.

T   F   5. Posting from a multicolumn purchases journal to an accounts payable ledger is done at the end of the month.

T   F   6. The purchases journal is used for the buying of merchandise for cash and on account.

T   F   7. When you post directly from the purchases invoice, you eliminate the accounts payable ledger.

T   F   8. The purchases journal contains an Accounts Payable Credit column, a Freight In Debit column, and a Purchases Debit column.

T F 9. Check marks in the Posting Reference column of the purchases journal indicate that the amounts in the Accounts Payable column have been posted to the accounts payable ledger.

T F 10. If the transportation terms are FOB destination, the cost of the freight charge is included in the selling price.

PART 2 Completion—Language of Business

Complete each of the following statements by writing the appropriate word(s) in the spaces provided:

1. The _____ account is used to record the transportation costs on incoming merchandise.
2. The form sent to the supplier of merchandise is called a(n) _____ .
3. When the buyer pays the transportation charges on incoming merchandise, the terms are called _____ .
4. Plans and procedures built into the accounting system to promote efficiency and prevent fraud and waste are called _____ .
5. Proving that total debits equal total credits in a multicolumn purchases journal is called _____ .
6. From the buyer's viewpoint, the form prepared by the seller listing the items shipped, their costs, and the mode of shipment is called a(n) _____ .
7. A document sent by the seller to the buyer, indicating that the Accounts Receivable account is being reduced on the seller's books, is known as a(n) _____ .
8. A transportation arrangement in which the seller retains title to the goods in transit is called _____ .

DEMONSTRATION PROBLEM

The following transactions were completed by Brownfield Company. The company is located in San Diego, California.

Aug. 3 Bought merchandise on account from Keller Company, invoice no. 1998, $5,544; 2/10, n/30; dated August 1; FOB Los Angeles, freight prepaid and added to the invoice, $554 (total $6,098).

10 Bought supplies on account from Nichols Company, invoice no. A1120, $572, net 30 days, dated August 10, FOB San Diego.

12 Received credit memo no. 170 from Keller Company, $640, for merchandise returned.

15 Bought merchandise on account from Lopez Company, invoice no. 3567C, $3,977; 1/10, n/30, dated August 12; FOB Reno; freight prepaid and added to the invoice, $380 ($4,357).

17 Received credit memo no. 435 from Nichols Company, $52, for allowance on damaged supplies purchased August 10.

Instructions

1. Record the transactions in either the three-column purchases journal or the general journal, as appropriate.
2. Post the entries to the accounts payable ledger daily.
3. Post the entries in the general journal immediately after you make each entry.
4. Post the totals from the three-column purchases journal at the end of the month.
5. Prepare a schedule of accounts payable.
6. Compare the total of the schedule of accounts payable with the balance of the controlling account.

SOLUTION

PURCHASES JOURNAL

DATE		SUPPLIER'S NAME	INV. NO.	INV. DATE	TERMS	POST. REF.	ACCOUNTS PAYABLE CREDIT	FREIGHT IN DEBIT	PURCHASES DEBIT
19—									
Aug.	3	Keller Company	1998	8/1	2/10,n/30	✓	6098 00	554 00	5544 00
	15	Lopez Company	3567C	8/12	1/10,n/30	✓	4357 00	380 00	3977 00
	31						10455 00	934 00	9521 00
							(212)	(514)	(511)

GENERAL JOURNAL

DATE		DESCRIPTION	POST. REF.	DEBIT	CREDIT
19—					
Aug.	10	Supplies	115	572 00	
		Accounts Payable, Nichols Company	212/✓		572 00
		Bought supplies on account, invoice			
		no. A1120, dated August 10, net			
		30 days.			
	12	Accounts Payable, Keller Company	212/✓	640 00	
		Purchases Returns and Allowances	512		640 00
		Credit memo no. 170 for merchandise			
		returned.			
	17	Accounts Payable, Nichols Company	212/✓	52 00	
		Supplies	115		52 00
		Credit memo no. 435 for allowance			
		on damaged supplies.			

GENERAL LEDGER

ACCOUNT __Supplies__   ACCOUNT NO. __115__

DATE		ITEM	POST. REF.	DEBIT	CREDIT	BALANCE DEBIT	BALANCE CREDIT
19—							
Aug.	1	Balance	✓			5790 00	
	10		J105	572 00		6362 00	
	17		J105		52 00	6310 00	

ACCOUNT _Accounts Payable_   ACCOUNT NO. 212

DATE		ITEM	POST. REF.	DEBIT	CREDIT	BALANCE DEBIT	BALANCE CREDIT
19—							
Aug.	1	Balance	✓				3 7 8 0 00
	10		J105		5 7 2 00		4 3 5 2 00
	12		J105	6 4 0 00			3 7 1 2 00
	17		J105	5 2 00			3 6 6 0 00
	31		P81		10 4 5 5 00		14 1 1 5 00

ACCOUNT _Purchases_   ACCOUNT NO. 511

DATE		ITEM	POST. REF.	DEBIT	CREDIT	BALANCE DEBIT	BALANCE CREDIT
19—							
Aug.	1	Balance	✓			73 1 8 5 00	
	31		P81	9 5 2 1 00		82 7 0 6 00	

ACCOUNT _Purchases Returns and Allowances_   ACCOUNT NO. 512

DATE		ITEM	POST. REF.	DEBIT	CREDIT	BALANCE DEBIT	BALANCE CREDIT
19—							
Aug.	1	Balance	✓				2 0 3 5 00
	12		J105		6 4 0 00		2 6 7 5 00

ACCOUNT _Freight In_   ACCOUNT NO. 514

DATE		ITEM	POST. REF.	DEBIT	CREDIT	BALANCE DEBIT	BALANCE CREDIT
19—							
Aug.	1	Balance	✓			7 4 5 9 00	
	31		P81	9 3 4 00		8 3 9 3 00	

ACCOUNTS PAYABLE LEDGER

NAME _Keller Company_

ADDRESS _679 Gurnard Ave._
Des Moines, IA 50371

DATE		ITEM	POST. REF.	DEBIT	CREDIT	BALANCE
19—						
Aug.	1	Balance	✓			1 9 7 0 00
	3		P81		6 0 9 8 00	8 0 6 8 00
	12		J105	6 4 0 00		7 4 2 8 00

NAME **Lopez Company**
ADDRESS **482 Jeffries Way**
Des Moines, IA 50372

DATE		ITEM	POST. REF.	DEBIT	CREDIT	BALANCE
19—						
Aug.	1	Balance	✓			1 8 1 0 00
	15		P81		4 3 5 7 00	6 1 6 7 00

NAME **Nichols Company**
ADDRESS **3864 Silva Ave.**
Des Moines, IA 50372

DATE		ITEM	POST. REF.	DEBIT	CREDIT	BALANCE
19—						
Aug.	10		J105		5 7 2 00	5 7 2 00
	17		J105	5 2 00		5 2 0 00

Brownfield Company
Schedule of Accounts Payable
August 31, 19—

Keller Company	$ 7 4 2 8 00
Lopez Company	6 1 6 7 00
Nichols Company	5 2 0 00
	$14 1 1 5 00

PROBLEM 12-1A or 12-1B

PURCHASES JOURNAL   PAGE _____

	DATE	SUPPLIER'S NAME	INV. NO.	INV. DATE	TERMS	POST. REF.	ACCOUNTS PAYABLE CREDIT	FREIGHT IN DEBIT	PURCHASES DEBIT	
1										1
2										2
3										3
4										4
5										5
6										6
7										7
8										8
9										9
10										10
11										11
12										12

GENERAL LEDGER

ACCOUNT _Accounts Payable_ _____ ACCOUNT NO. _212_

DATE	ITEM	POST. REF.	DEBIT	CREDIT	BALANCE DEBIT	BALANCE CREDIT

ACCOUNT _Purchases_ _____ ACCOUNT NO. _511_

DATE	ITEM	POST. REF.	DEBIT	CREDIT	BALANCE DEBIT	BALANCE CREDIT

ACCOUNT _Freight In_ _____ ACCOUNT NO. _514_

DATE	ITEM	POST. REF.	DEBIT	CREDIT	BALANCE DEBIT	BALANCE CREDIT

PROBLEM 12-1A or 12-1B (continued)

ACCOUNTS PAYABLE LEDGER

NAME _____

ADDRESS _____

	DATE		ITEM	POST. REF.	DEBIT	CREDIT	BALANCE

NAME _____

ADDRESS _____

	DATE		ITEM	POST. REF.	DEBIT	CREDIT	BALANCE

NAME _____

ADDRESS _____

	DATE		ITEM	POST. REF.	DEBIT	CREDIT	BALANCE

NAME _____

ADDRESS _____

	DATE		ITEM	POST. REF.	DEBIT	CREDIT	BALANCE

PROBLEM 12-1A or 12-1B (concluded)

NAME _____

ADDRESS _____

_____

	DATE	ITEM	POST. REF.	DEBIT	CREDIT	BALANCE

NAME _____

ADDRESS _____

_____

	DATE	ITEM	POST. REF.	DEBIT	CREDIT	BALANCE

PROBLEM 12-2A or 12-2B

PURCHASES JOURNAL

PAGE _____

DATE	SUPPLIER'S NAME	INVOICE NUMBER	INVOICE DATE	TERMS	POST. REF.	ACCOUNTS PAYABLE CREDIT	PURCHASES DEBIT	FREIGHT IN DEBIT	STORE SUPPLIES DEBIT	OFFICE SUPPLIES DEBIT	OTHER ACCOUNTS DEBIT		
											ACCOUNT	POST. REF.	AMOUNT

PROBLEM 12-2A or 12-2B (continued)

GENERAL JOURNAL   PAGE _____

	DATE	DESCRIPTION	POST. REF.	DEBIT	CREDIT	
1						1
2						2
3						3
4						4
5						5
6						6
7						7
8						8
9						9
10						10
11						11
12						12
13						13
14						14
15						15
16						16
17						17
18						18
19						19
20						20
21						21
22						22
23						23
24						24
25						25
26						26
27						27
28						28
29						29
30						30
31						31
32						32
33						33
34						34
35						35
36						36
37						37

PROBLEM 12-2A or 12-2B (continued)

GENERAL LEDGER

ACCOUNT _Store Supplies_ _____ ACCOUNT NO. _114_

DATE		ITEM	POST. REF.	DEBIT	CREDIT	BALANCE	
						DEBIT	CREDIT
19—							
July	1	Balance	✓			3 9 2 16	

ACCOUNT _Office Supplies_ _____ ACCOUNT NO. _115_

DATE		ITEM	POST. REF.	DEBIT	CREDIT	BALANCE	
						DEBIT	CREDIT
19—							
July	1	Balance	✓			1 5 1 10	

ACCOUNT _Equipment_ _____ ACCOUNT NO. _124_

DATE		ITEM	POST. REF.	DEBIT	CREDIT	BALANCE	
						DEBIT	CREDIT
19—							
July	1	Balance	✓			43 7 1 6 00	

ACCOUNT _Accounts Payable_ _____ ACCOUNT NO. _212_

DATE		ITEM	POST. REF.	DEBIT	CREDIT	BALANCE	
						DEBIT	CREDIT
19—							
July	1	Balance	✓				3 1 8 2 45

PROBLEM 12-2A or 12-2B (continued)

ACCOUNT **Purchases** ACCOUNT NO. *511*

DATE		ITEM	POST. REF.	DEBIT	CREDIT	BALANCE	
						DEBIT	CREDIT
19—							
July	1	Balance	✓			36 4 1 7 60	

ACCOUNT **Purchases Returns and Allowances** ACCOUNT NO. *512*

DATE		ITEM	POST. REF.	DEBIT	CREDIT	BALANCE	
						DEBIT	CREDIT
19—							
July	1	Balance	✓				1 4 0 5 55

ACCOUNT **Freight In** ACCOUNT NO. *514*

DATE		ITEM	POST. REF.	DEBIT	CREDIT	BALANCE	
						DEBIT	CREDIT
19—							
July	1	Balance	✓			2 7 2 2 94	

ACCOUNTS PAYABLE LEDGER

NAME _____

ADDRESS _____

DATE		ITEM	POST. REF.	DEBIT	CREDIT	BALANCE	

PROBLEM 12-2A or 12-2B (continued)

NAME _____

ADDRESS _____

_____

DATE		ITEM	POST. REF.	DEBIT	CREDIT	BALANCE

NAME _____

ADDRESS _____

_____

DATE		ITEM	POST. REF.	DEBIT	CREDIT	BALANCE

NAME _____

ADDRESS _____

_____

DATE		ITEM	POST. REF.	DEBIT	CREDIT	BALANCE

NAME _____

ADDRESS _____

_____

DATE		ITEM	POST. REF.	DEBIT	CREDIT	BALANCE

PROBLEM 12-2A or 12-2B (concluded)

NAME _____

ADDRESS _____

_____

	DATE		ITEM	POST. REF.	DEBIT			CREDIT			BALANCE		

NAME _____

ADDRESS _____

_____

	DATE		ITEM	POST. REF.	DEBIT			CREDIT			BALANCE		

_____

_____

PROBLEM 12-3A or 12-3B

GENERAL JOURNAL   PAGE _____

	DATE		DESCRIPTION	POST. REF.	DEBIT	CREDIT	
1							1
2							2
3							3
4							4
5							5
6							6
7							7
8							8
9							9
10							10
11							11
12							12
13							13
14							14
15							15
16							16

PROBLEM 12-4A or 12-4B

SALES JOURNAL

	DATE	INV. NO.	CUSTOMER'S NAME	POST. REF.	ACCOUNTS RECEIVABLE DR., SALES CR.	
1						1
2						2
3						3
4						4
5						5
6						6
7						7
8						8

PURCHASES JOURNAL

	DATE	SUPPLIER'S NAME	INV. NO.	INV. DATE	TERMS	POST. REF.	ACCOUNTS PAYABLE CREDIT	FREIGHT IN DEBIT	PURCHASES DEBIT	
1										1
2										2
3										3
4										4
5										5
6										6
7										7

PROBLEM 12-4A or 12-4B (continued)

GENERAL JOURNAL

	DATE		DESCRIPTION	POST. REF.	DEBIT	CREDIT	
1							1
2							2
3							3
4							4
5							5
6							6
7							7
8							8
9							9
10							10
11							11
12							12
13							13
14							14
15							15
16							16
17							17
18							18
19							19
20							20
21							21
22							22

ACCOUNTS RECEIVABLE LEDGER

NAME _____

ADDRESS _____

_____

DATE	ITEM	POST. REF.	DEBIT	CREDIT	BALANCE

PROBLEM 12-4A or 12-4B (continued)

NAME _____

ADDRESS _____

DATE	ITEM	POST. REF.	DEBIT	CREDIT	BALANCE

NAME _____

ADDRESS _____

DATE	ITEM	POST. REF.	DEBIT	CREDIT	BALANCE

NAME _____

ADDRESS _____

DATE	ITEM	POST. REF.	DEBIT	CREDIT	BALANCE

ACCOUNTS PAYABLE LEDGER

NAME _____

ADDRESS _____

DATE	ITEM	POST. REF.	DEBIT	CREDIT	BALANCE

PROBLEM 12-4A or 12-4B (continued)

NAME _____

ADDRESS _____

DATE	ITEM	POST. REF.	DEBIT	CREDIT	BALANCE

NAME _____

ADDRESS _____

DATE	ITEM	POST. REF.	DEBIT	CREDIT	BALANCE

NAME _____

ADDRESS _____

DATE	ITEM	POST. REF.	DEBIT	CREDIT	BALANCE

NAME _____

ADDRESS _____

DATE	ITEM	POST. REF.	DEBIT	CREDIT	BALANCE

PROBLEM 12-4A or 12-4B (continued)

GENERAL LEDGER

ACCOUNT _Accounts Receivable_ _____ ACCOUNT NO. _113_

DATE		ITEM	POST. REF.	DEBIT	CREDIT	BALANCE	
						DEBIT	CREDIT
19—							
June	1	Balance	√			1 871 00	

ACCOUNT _Office Supplies_ _____ ACCOUNT NO. _115_

DATE		ITEM	POST. REF.	DEBIT	CREDIT	BALANCE	
						DEBIT	CREDIT
19—							
June	1	Balance	√			430 00	

ACCOUNT _Accounts Payable_ _____ ACCOUNT NO. _212_

DATE		ITEM	POST. REF.	DEBIT	CREDIT	BALANCE	
						DEBIT	CREDIT
19—							
June	1	Balance	√				609 00

ACCOUNT _Sales_ _____ ACCOUNT NO. _411_

DATE		ITEM	POST. REF.	DEBIT	CREDIT	BALANCE	
						DEBIT	CREDIT
19—							
June	1	Balance	√				38 261 00

PROBLEM 12-4A or 12-4B (continued)

ACCOUNT *Sales Returns and Allowances* _____ ACCOUNT NO. **412**

DATE		ITEM	POST. REF.	DEBIT	CREDIT	BALANCE	
						DEBIT	CREDIT
19—							
June	1	Balance	√			1 6 7 0 00	

ACCOUNT *Purchases* _____ ACCOUNT NO. **511**

DATE		ITEM	POST. REF.	DEBIT	CREDIT	BALANCE	
						DEBIT	CREDIT
19—							
June	1	Balance	√			29 6 4 0 00	

ACCOUNT *Purchases Returns and Allowances* _____ ACCOUNT NO. **512**

DATE		ITEM	POST. REF.	DEBIT	CREDIT	BALANCE	
						DEBIT	CREDIT
19—							
June	1	Balance	√				7 2 0 00

ACCOUNT *Freight In* _____ ACCOUNT NO. **514**

DATE		ITEM	POST. REF.	DEBIT	CREDIT	BALANCE	
						DEBIT	CREDIT
19—							
June	1	Balance	√			9 2 2 00	

PROBLEM 12-4A or 12-4B (concluded)

Cash Receipts and Cash Payments

LEARNING OBJECTIVES

1. Record transactions for a retail merchandising business in a cash receipts journal.
2. Post from a cash receipts journal to a general ledger and an accounts receivable ledger.
3. Determine cash discounts according to credit terms, and record cash receipts from charge customers who are entitled to deduct the cash discount.
4. Record transactions in a cash payments journal for a service enterprise.
5. Record transactions in a cash payments journal for a merchandising enterprise involving cash discounts.
6. Record transactions in a check register.
7. Record transactions involving trade discounts.

KEY TERMS

Bank charge card   Check register
Cash discount   Credit period
Cash payments journal   Sales discount
Cash receipts journal   Trade discount

STUDY GUIDE QUESTIONS

PART 1   True/False

For each of the following statements, circle T if the statement is true and F if the statement is false.

T   F   1. The normal balance of the Sales Discount account is on the debit side.

T   F   2. An investment of cash by the owner is always recorded in the general journal.

T   F   3. In a cash receipts journal, the individual amounts in the Other Accounts column are posted at the end of the month.

T   F   4. Entries in the Accounts Payable Debit column of a cash payments journal are posted daily to the accounts payable ledger.

T   F   5. The Purchases Discount account is classified as a revenue account.

T   F   6. Credit terms of 1/10, n/30 indicate that a discount of one-tenth may be deducted if the bill is paid in thirty days.

T   F   7. The amount of the discount that the bank deducts for a credit card transaction is usually between 10 and 15 percent.

T   F   8. The buyer records the purchases discount when payment is made.

T   F   9. Trade discounts are not recorded on the books of either the buyer or the seller.

T   F   10. A check register performs the same function as a cash payments journal.

PART 2 Completion—Language of Business

Complete each of the following statements by writing the appropriate word(s) in the spaces provided:

1. Large deductions from the list prices of merchandise are referred to as _____ _____ .

2. The time the seller allows the buyer before full payment on a charge sale has to be made is called the _____ .

3. The _____ is the amount a customer may deduct for paying a bill within a specified period of time.

PART 3 Matching

For each numbered item, choose the appropriate journal and write the identifying letter.

_____ 1. Bought merchandise on account

_____ 2. Sold merchandise for cash

_____ 3. Recorded supplies used

_____ 4. Collected accounts receivable and allowed a cash discount

_____ 5. Bought store equipment on credit

_____ 6. Recorded accrued wages

_____ 7. Received credit memo for merchandise returned

_____ 8. Paid freight bill on merchandise purchased

_____ 9. Sold merchandise on account

_____ 10. Paid state unemployment tax

S   Sales journal
P   Purchases journal (3 columns)
CR   Cash receipts journal
CP   Cash payments journal
J   General journal

PART 4 Cash Receipts Journal

Label the money columns as Debit or Credit.

Other Accounts	Accounts Receivable	Sales	Sales Discount	Cash

DEMONSTRATION PROBLEM

Elegant Jewelry, a retail store, sells merchandise (1) for cash, (2) on charge accounts, and (3) on bank credit cards. The store uses a sales journal, a purchases journal, a cash receipts journal, a cash payments journal, and a general journal. The store engaged in the following selected transactions:

June 16 Sold merchandise on account to T. Morgan, sales ticket no. 1230, $9,757, plus $487.85 sales tax.

17 Total sales paid by bank credit cards, $2,271, plus $183.95 sales tax. The bank charges 4 percent of the total sales plus sales tax.

18 Bought merchandise on account from Gem Central, invoice no. D109, dated June 16; $4,542; terms 1/10, n/30; FOB shipping point, freight prepaid and added to the invoice, $60 (total, $4,602).

19 Received credit memorandum no. 926 from Gem Central for merchandise return, $529.

22 Paid Gem Central, their invoice no. D109, Ck. No. 5901, $4,032.87. ($4,542 less $529 return and less 1 percent cash discount. $4,542.00 − $529.00 = $4,013.00; $4,013.00 × .01 = $40.13; $4,013.00 − $40.13 = $3,972.87; $3,972.87 + $60 freight = $4,032.87.)

24 Bought packaging supplies on account from The Box Company, their invoice no. 990, dated June 22; net 30 days; $459.

29 Paid rent for the month, Ck. No. 5902, $1,980.

30 Bought merchandise on account from Todd Company, their invoice no. 10002, dated June 29; list price $2,950, less 40 percent trade discount; terms 2/10, n/30; FOB destination.

30 Paid freight bill to Fast Freight, Ck. No. 5903, for merchandise received from Todd Company, $110.

30 Issued Ck. No. 5904 for $258.36 to customer L. O. Sherry, for merchandise returned, $239, plus $19.36 sales tax.

Instructions

1. Journalize the transactions.
2. Total and rule the journals.
3. Prove the equality of the debits and credits at the bottom of each journal.

SOLUTION

SALES JOURNAL

DATE		TKT. NO.	CUSTOMER'S NAME	POST. REF.	ACCOUNTS RECEIVABLE DEBIT	SALES TAX PAYABLE CREDIT	SALES CREDIT
19—							
June	16	1230	T. Morgan		10 2 4 4 85	4 8 7 85	9 7 5 7 00
	30				10 2 4 4 85	4 8 7 85	9 7 5 7 00

Debits	Credits
$10,244.85	$ 487.85
	9,757.00
$10,244.85	$10,244.85

PURCHASES JOURNAL

DATE	SUPPLIER'S NAME	INV. NO.	INV. DATE	TERMS	POST. REF.	ACCOUNTS PAYABLE CREDIT	FREIGHT IN DEBIT	PURCHASES DEBIT
19—								
June 18	Gem Central	D109	6/16	1/10, n/30		4602 00	60 00	4542 00
30	Todd Company	10002	6/29	2/10, n/30		1770 00		1770 00
30						6372 00	60 00	6312 00

Debits   Credits
$ 60.00 $6,372.00
6,312.00

$6,372.00 $6,372.00

CASH RECEIPTS JOURNAL

DATE	ACCOUNT CREDITED	POST. REF.	OTHER ACCOUNTS CREDIT	ACCOUNTS RECEIVABLE CREDIT	SALES CREDIT	SALES TAX PAYABLE CREDIT	CREDIT CARD EXPENSE DEBIT	CASH DEBIT
19—								
June 17	Sales				2271 00	183 95	98 20	2356 75
30					2271 00	183 95	98 20	2356 75

Debits   Credits
$ 98.20 $2,271.00
2,356.75   183.95

$2,454.95 $2,454.95

CASH PAYMENTS JOURNAL

DATE	CK. NO.	ACCOUNT NAME	POST. REF.	OTHER ACCOUNTS DEBIT	ACCOUNTS PAYABLE DEBIT	PURCHASES DISCOUNT CREDIT	CASH CREDIT
19—							
June 22	5901	Gem Central			4073 00	40 13	4032 87
29	5902	Rent Expense		1980 00			1980 00
30	5903	Freight In		110 00			110 00
30	5904	Sales Returns and Allow.		239 00			
		Sales Tax Payable		19 36			258 36
30				2348 36	4073 00	40 13	6381 23

Debits   Credits
$2,348.36 $ 40.13
4,073.00   6,381.23

$6,421.36 $6,421.36

DATE		DESCRIPTION	POST. REF.	DEBIT				CREDIT			
19—											
June	19	Accounts Payable, Gem Central		5	2	9	00				
		Purchases Returns and Allowances						5	2	9	00
		Credit memo no. 926.									
	24	Supplies		4	5	9	00				
		Accounts Payable, The Box Co.						4	5	9	00
		Packing supplies, invoice									
		no. 990, dated June 22,									
		net 30 days.									

PROBLEM 13-1A or 13-1B

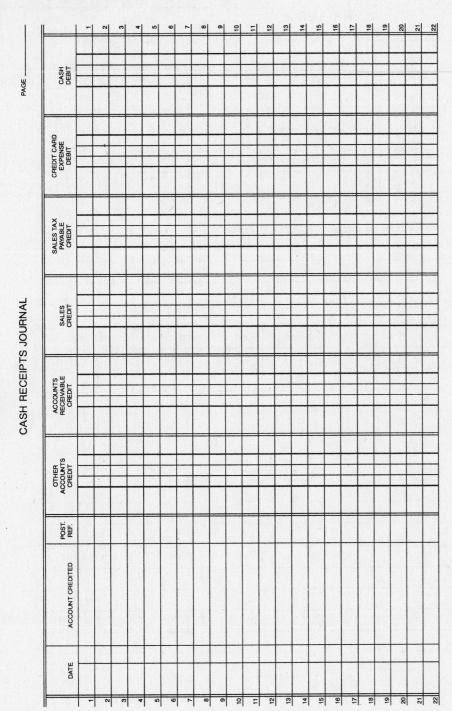

CASH RECEIPTS JOURNAL

PAGE _____

PROBLEM 13-1A or 13-1B (continued)

GENERAL LEDGER

ACCOUNT *Accounts Receivable*   ACCOUNT NO. *113*

DATE	ITEM	POST. REF.	DEBIT	CREDIT	BALANCE	
					DEBIT	CREDIT

ACCOUNTS RECEIVABLE LEDGER

NAME _____

ADDRESS _____

_____

DATE	ITEM	POST. REF.	DEBIT	CREDIT	BALANCE

NAME _____

ADDRESS _____

_____

DATE	ITEM	POST. REF.	DEBIT	CREDIT	BALANCE

PROBLEM 13-1A or 13-1B (concluded)

NAME _____

ADDRESS _____

	DATE	ITEM	POST. REF.	DEBIT	CREDIT	BALANCE

NAME _____

ADDRESS _____

	DATE	ITEM	POST. REF.	DEBIT	CREDIT	BALANCE

NAME _____

ADDRESS _____

	DATE	ITEM	POST. REF.	DEBIT	CREDIT	BALANCE

NAME _____

ADDRESS _____

	DATE	ITEM	POST. REF.	DEBIT	CREDIT	BALANCE

PROBLEM 13-2A or 13-2B

CASH RECEIPTS JOURNAL

PAGE ___ 71

DATE	ACCOUNT CREDITED	POST. REF.	OTHER ACCOUNTS CREDIT	ACCOUNTS RECEIVABLE CREDIT	SALES CREDIT	SALES DISCOUNT DEBIT	CASH DEBIT
1							
2							
3							
4							
5							
6							
7							
8							
9							
10							
11							
12							
13							

SALES JOURNAL

PAGE ___ 43

DATE	INV. NO.	CUSTOMER'S NAME	POST. REF.	ACCOUNTS RECEIVABLE DR., SALES CR.
1				
2				
3				
4				
5				
6				

216

PROBLEM 13-3A or 13-3B

PAGE ___ 27

CHECK REGISTER

DATE	CK. NO.	PAYEE	ACCOUNT DEBITED	POST. REF.	OTHER ACCOUNTS DEBIT	ACCOUNTS PAYABLE DEBIT	PURCHASES DISCOUNT CREDIT	FIRST NATL BANK CREDIT

PROBLEM 13-4A or 13-4B

SALES JOURNAL

PAGE _____

	DATE	INV. NO.	CUSTOMER'S NAME	POST. REF.	ACCOUNTS RECEIVABLE DR., SALES CR.	
1						1
2						2
3						3
4						4
5						5
6						6
7						7
8						8

PURCHASES JOURNAL

PAGE _____

	DATE	SUPPLIER'S NAME	INV. NO.	INV. DATE	TERMS	POST. REF.	ACCOUNTS PAYABLE CREDIT	FREIGHT IN DEBIT	PURCHASES DEBIT	
1										1
2										2
3										3
4										4
5										5
6										6

PROBLEM 13-4A or 13-4B (continued)

PAGE _____

CASH RECEIPTS JOURNAL

DATE	ACCOUNT CREDITED	POST. REF.	OTHER ACCOUNTS CREDIT	ACCOUNTS RECEIVABLE CREDIT	SALES CREDIT	SALES DISCOUNT DEBIT	CASH DEBIT

PROBLEM 13-4A or 13-4B (continued)

PAGE _____

CASH PAYMENTS JOURNAL

DATE	CK. NO.	ACCOUNT NAME	POST. REF.	OTHER ACCOUNTS DEBIT	ACCOUNTS PAYABLE DEBIT	PURCHASES DISCOUNT CREDIT	CASH CREDIT

PROBLEM 13-4A or 13-B (continued)

GENERAL JOURNAL   PAGE _____

	DATE	DESCRIPTION	POST. REF.	DEBIT	CREDIT	
1						1
2						2
3						3
4						4
5						5
6						6
7						7
8						8
9						9
10						10
11						11
12						12
13						13
14						14
15						15
16						16
17						17
18						18
19						19
20						20
21						21
22						22
23						23
24						24
25						25
26						26
27						27
28						28
29						29
30						30
31						31
32						32
33						33
34						34
35						35
36						36
37						37

PROBLEM 13-4A or 13-4B (continued)

GENERAL LEDGER

ACCOUNT _Cash_ _____ ACCOUNT NO. _111_

DATE		ITEM	POST. REF.	DEBIT	CREDIT	BALANCE	
						DEBIT	CREDIT
19—							
Jan.	1	Balance	✓			13 1 1 0 00	

ACCOUNT _Accounts Receivable_ _____ ACCOUNT NO. _113_

DATE		ITEM	POST. REF.	DEBIT	CREDIT	BALANCE	
						DEBIT	CREDIT
19—							
Jan.	1	Balance	✓			2 4 7 5 00	

ACCOUNT _Merchandise Inventory_ _____ ACCOUNT NO. _114_

DATE		ITEM	POST. REF.	DEBIT	CREDIT	BALANCE	
						DEBIT	CREDIT
19—							
Jan.	1	Balance	✓			30 8 7 6 00	

PROBLEM 13-4A or 13-4B (continued)

GENERAL LEDGER

ACCOUNT _Supplies_ _____ ACCOUNT NO. _115_

DATE		ITEM	POST. REF.	DEBIT	CREDIT	BALANCE	
						DEBIT	CREDIT
19—							
Jan.	1	Balance	✓			888 00	

ACCOUNT _Prepaid Insurance_ _____ ACCOUNT NO. _116_

DATE		ITEM	POST. REF.	DEBIT	CREDIT	BALANCE	
						DEBIT	CREDIT
19—							
Jan.	1	Balance	✓			585 00	

ACCOUNT _Equipment_ _____ ACCOUNT NO. _121_

DATE		ITEM	POST. REF.	DEBIT	CREDIT	BALANCE	
						DEBIT	CREDIT
19—							
Jan.	1	Balance	✓			5466 00	

ACCOUNT _Accounts Payable_ _____ ACCOUNT NO. _212_

DATE		ITEM	POST. REF.	DEBIT	CREDIT	BALANCE	
						DEBIT	CREDIT
19—							
Jan.	1	Balance	✓				900 00

PROBLEM 13-4A or 13-4B (continued)

ACCOUNT *Salaries Payable*　ACCOUNT NO. *215*

DATE	ITEM	POST. REF.	DEBIT	CREDIT	BALANCE	
					DEBIT	CREDIT

ACCOUNT *Employee's Federal Income Tax Payable*　ACCOUNT NO. *216*

DATE	ITEM	POST. REF.	DEBIT	CREDIT	BALANCE	
					DEBIT	CREDIT

ACCOUNT *FICA Tax Payable*　ACCOUNT NO. *217*

DATE	ITEM	POST. REF.	DEBIT	CREDIT	BALANCE	
					DEBIT	CREDIT

ACCOUNT *State Unemployment Tax Payable*　ACCOUNT NO. *218*

DATE	ITEM	POST. REF.	DEBIT	CREDIT	BALANCE	
					DEBIT	CREDIT

PROBLEM 13-4A or 13-4B (continued)

ACCOUNT _Federal Unemployment Tax Payable_   ACCOUNT NO. _219_

DATE	ITEM	POST. REF.	DEBIT	CREDIT	BALANCE DEBIT	BALANCE CREDIT

ACCOUNT _C. M. Marsh, Capital_   ACCOUNT NO. _311_

DATE	ITEM	POST. REF.	DEBIT	CREDIT	BALANCE DEBIT	BALANCE CREDIT
19—						
Jan. 1	Balance	√				52 500 00

ACCOUNT _C. M. Marsh, Drawing_   ACCOUNT NO. _312_

DATE	ITEM	POST. REF.	DEBIT	CREDIT	BALANCE DEBIT	BALANCE CREDIT

ACCOUNT _Sales_   ACCOUNT NO. _411_

DATE	ITEM	POST. REF.	DEBIT	CREDIT	BALANCE DEBIT	BALANCE CREDIT

PROBLEM 13-4A or 13-4B (continued)

ACCOUNT _Sales Returns and Allowances_   ACCOUNT NO. _412_

DATE	ITEM	POST. REF.	DEBIT	CREDIT	BALANCE DEBIT	BALANCE CREDIT

ACCOUNT _Sales Discount_   ACCOUNT NO. _413_

DATE	ITEM	POST. REF.	DEBIT	CREDIT	BALANCE DEBIT	BALANCE CREDIT

ACCOUNT _Purchases_   ACCOUNT NO. _511_

DATE	ITEM	POST. REF.	DEBIT	CREDIT	BALANCE DEBIT	BALANCE CREDIT

ACCOUNT _Purchases Returns and Allowances_   ACCOUNT NO. _512_

DATE	ITEM	POST. REF.	DEBIT	CREDIT	BALANCE DEBIT	BALANCE CREDIT

PROBLEM 13-4A or 13-4B (continued)

ACCOUNT *Purchases Discount* _____ ACCOUNT NO. *513*

DATE	ITEM	POST. REF.	DEBIT	CREDIT	BALANCE	
					DEBIT	CREDIT

ACCOUNT *Freight In* _____ ACCOUNT NO. *514*

DATE	ITEM	POST. REF.	DEBIT	CREDIT	BALANCE	
					DEBIT	CREDIT

ACCOUNT *Salary Expense* _____ ACCOUNT NO. *521*

DATE	ITEM	POST. REF.	DEBIT	CREDIT	BALANCE	
					DEBIT	CREDIT

ACCOUNT *Payroll Tax Expense* _____ ACCOUNT NO. *522*

DATE	ITEM	POST. REF.	DEBIT	CREDIT	BALANCE	
					DEBIT	CREDIT

ACCOUNT *Rent Expense* _____ ACCOUNT NO. *527*

DATE	ITEM	POST. REF.	DEBIT	CREDIT	BALANCE	
					DEBIT	CREDIT

PROBLEM 13-4A or 13-4B (continued)

ACCOUNT *Miscellaneous Expense* _____ ACCOUNT NO. *531*

DATE	ITEM	POST. REF.	DEBIT	CREDIT	BALANCE	
					DEBIT	CREDIT

ACCOUNTS RECEIVABLE LEDGER

NAME *Burke Supply*
ADDRESS *1620 Fleming Blvd.*
Denver, CO 80294

DATE	ITEM	POST. REF.	DEBIT	CREDIT	BALANCE

NAME *Eaton and Sievert*
ADDRESS *482 E. Marion Road*
Denver, CO 80279

DATE	ITEM	POST. REF.	DEBIT	CREDIT	BALANCE

NAME *F.C. Parket*
ADDRESS *1764 N. Maynard Ave.*
Denver, CO 80279

DATE	ITEM	POST. REF.	DEBIT	CREDIT	BALANCE

PROBLEM 13-4A or 13-4B (continued)

NAME _Pike and Secord_

ADDRESS _4682 N. Roberts Ave._

Denver, CO 80284

DATE		ITEM	POST. REF.	DEBIT	CREDIT	BALANCE
19—						
Jan.	1	Balance	✓			975 00

NAME _Vanguard Appliance_

ADDRESS _460 S. Sinclair Ave._

Denver, CO 80281

DATE		ITEM	POST. REF.	DEBIT	CREDIT	BALANCE
19—						
Jan.	1	Balance	✓			1500 00

PROBLEM 13-4A or 13-4B (continued)

ACCOUNTS PAYABLE LEDGER

NAME _Collins Products_

ADDRESS _1200 Staples Blvd._
Denver, CO 80291

DATE	ITEM	POST. REF.	DEBIT	CREDIT	BALANCE

NAME _Dempsey Office Supply_

ADDRESS _420 Sutton Place_
Boulder, CO 80364

DATE	ITEM	POST. REF.	DEBIT	CREDIT	BALANCE

NAME _Franz Company_

ADDRESS _140 S. McGrath Ave._
Kansas City, KS 66189

DATE	ITEM	POST. REF.	DEBIT	CREDIT	BALANCE
19—					
Jan. 1	Balance	✓			9 0 0 00

NAME _Vargas and Company_

ADDRESS _2400 Miller Way_
South Bend, IN 46692

DATE	ITEM	POST. REF.	DEBIT	CREDIT	BALANCE

PROBLEM 13-4A or 13-4B (continued)

Marsh Electronics Supply

Trial Balance

January 31, 19—

ACCOUNT NAME	DEBIT	CREDIT
Cash		
Accounts Receivable		
Merchandise Inventory		
Supplies		
Prepaid Insurance		
Equipment		
Accounts Payable		
Employees' Federal Income Tax Payable		
FICA Tax Payable		
State Unemployment Tax Payable		
Federal Unemployment Tax Payable		
C. M. Marsh, Capital		
C. M. Marsh, Drawing		
Sales		
Sales Returns and Allowances		
Sales Discount		
Purchases		
Purchases Returns and Allowances		
Purchases Discount		
Freight In		
Salary Expense		
Payroll Tax Expense		
Rent Expense		
Miscellaneous Expense		

PROBLEM 13-4A or 13-4B (concluded)

Marsh Electronics Supply

Schedule of Accounts Receivable

January 31, 19—

Marsh Electronics Supply

Schedule of Accounts Payable

January 31, 19—

Work Sheet and Adjusting Entries for a Merchandising Business

LEARNING OBJECTIVES

1. Prepare an adjustment for merchandise inventory.
2. Prepare an adjustment for unearned revenue.
3. Record the adjustment data in a work sheet (including merchandise inventory, unearned revenue, supplies used, expired insurance, depreciation, and accrued wages or salaries).
4. Complete the work sheet.
5. Journalize the adjusting entries for a merchandising business.

KEY TERMS

Physical inventory (periodic inventory)
Unearned revenue

STUDY GUIDE QUESTIONS

PART 1   True/False

For each of the following statements, circle T if the statement is true and F if the statement is false.

T   F   1. An actual count of a stock of goods on hand is called a physical inventory.

T   F   2. The first adjustment for Merchandise Inventory is to debit Merchandise Inventory for the amount of the beginning inventory.

T   F   3. The value of the ending Merchandise Inventory appears in the Balance Sheet Credit column of the work sheet.

T   F   4. The balance of Sales Discount appears in the Income Statement Credit column.

T   F   5. Under the periodic inventory system, entries are recorded in the Merchandise Inventory account at the end of the fiscal period only.

T   F   6. When a business receives cash for a product or service that is to be delivered in the future, the Unearned Revenue account is credited.

T   F   7. The balance of the Unearned Revenue account appears in the Balance Sheet Credit column.

T   F   8. In the Balance Sheet columns of the work sheet, Income Summary is shown in two figures.

T   F   9. The balance of Purchases Discount appears in the Income Statement Credit column.

T   F   10. If Income Summary has a debit of $80,000 and a credit of $70,000 in the Adjustments columns of the work sheet, these will be combined into a debit of $10,000 in the Income Statement Debit column.

PART 2 Identifying Work Sheet Columns

Below is a list of selected accounts. Using a check mark, identify the columns in which the balance of each of the accounts would appear.

Account Name	Income Statement		Balance Sheet	
	Debit	Credit	Debit	Credit
Example: 0. Rent Income		√		
1. Sales Discount				
2. C. Carr, Drawing				
3. Supplies Expense				
4. Sales				
5. Merchandise Inventory				
6. Purchases Returns and Allowances				
7. Income Summary				
8. C. Carr, Capital				
9. Accumulated Depreciation, Equipment				
10. Purchases				
11. Sales Returns and Allowances				
12. Purchases Discount				
13. Unearned Rent				
14. Supplies				
15. Salaries Payable				

DEMONSTRATION PROBLEM

Office Specialists sells and services copiers and FAX machines. The trial balance as of December 31, the end of its fiscal year, is as follows:

Office Specialists

Trial Balance

December 31, 19—

ACCOUNT NAME	DEBIT	CREDIT
Cash	4 000 00	
Merchandise Inventory	151 000 00	
Supplies	2 000 00	
Prepaid Insurance	1 000 00	
Store Equipment	26 000 00	
Accumulated Depreciation, Store Equipment		12 500 00
Accounts Payable		50 000 00
Employees' Income Tax Payable		3 000 00
Payroll Taxes and Employees' Withholding Payable		1 500 00
Unearned Service Contracts		15 000 00
L. Griswald, Capital		44 100 00
L. Griswald, Drawing	60 000 00	
Sales		453 000 00
Service Contract Income		56 000 00
Purchases	280 000 00	
Purchases Discount		3 800 00
Freight In	3 900 00	
Salary Expense	80 000 00	
Payroll Tax Expense	8 000 00	
Rent Expense	20 000 00	
Miscellaneous Expense	3 000 00	
	638 900 00	638 900 00

The earnings from short-term contracts completed during the year have been recorded in Service Contract Income. Amounts received in advance for longer-term service contracts have been recorded in Unearned Service Contracts. To save space by reducing the number of accounts, we use the account called Payroll Taxes and Employees' Withholding Payable for the FICA and unemployment tax liabilities. Data for the adjustments are as follows:

a–b. Merchandise inventory at December 31, $139,500.
  c. Supplies inventory, $1,700.
  d. Insurance expired, $600.
  e. Salaries accrued, $2,000.
  f. Depreciation of store equipment, $5,200.
  g. Unearned service contract income now earned, $4,800.

Instructions

Complete the work sheet.

SOLUTION

	ACCOUNT NAME	TRIAL BALANCE DEBIT	TRIAL BALANCE CREDIT
1	Cash	4 0 0 0 00	
2	Merchandise Inventory	151 0 0 0 00	
3	Supplies	2 0 0 0 00	
4	Prepaid Insurance	1 0 0 0 00	
5	Store Equipment	26 0 0 0 00	
6	Accumulated Depreciation, Store Equipment		12 5 0 0 00
7	Accounts Payable		50 0 0 0 00
8	Employees' Income Tax Payable		3 0 0 0 00
9	Payroll Taxes and Employees' Withholding Payable		1 5 0 0 00
10	Unearned Service Contracts		15 0 0 0 00
11	L. Griswald, Capital		44 1 0 0 00
12	L. Griswald, Drawing	60 0 0 0 00	
13	Sales		453 0 0 0 00
14	Service Contract Income		56 0 0 0 00
15	Purchases	280 0 0 0 00	
16	Purchases Discount		3 8 0 0 00
17	Freight In	3 9 0 0 00	
18	Salary Expense	80 0 0 0 00	
19	Payroll Tax Expense	8 0 0 0 00	
20	Rent Expense	20 0 0 0 00	
21	Miscellaneous Expense	3 0 0 0 00	
22		638 9 0 0 00	638 9 0 0 00
23	Income Summary		
24	Supplies Expense		
25	Insurance Expense		
26	Salaries Payable		
27	Depreciation Expense, Store Equipment		
28			
29	Net Income		
30			
31			

ADJUSTMENTS DEBIT	ADJUSTMENTS CREDIT	INCOME STATEMENT DEBIT	INCOME STATEMENT CREDIT	BALANCE SHEET DEBIT	BALANCE SHEET CREDIT	
(b)	(a)			4 0 0 0 00		1
139 5 0 0 00	151 0 0 0 00			139 5 0 0 00		2
	(c) 3 0 0 00			1 7 0 0 00		3
	(d) 6 0 0 00			4 0 0 00		4
				26 0 0 0 00		5
	(f) 5 2 0 0 00				17 7 0 0 00	6
					50 0 0 0 00	7
					3 0 0 0 00	8
					1 5 0 0 00	9
(g) 4 8 0 0 00					10 2 0 0 00	10
					44 1 0 0 00	11
				60 0 0 0 00		12
			453 0 0 0 00			13
	(g) 4 8 0 0 00		60 8 0 0 00			14
		280 0 0 0 00				15
			3 8 0 0 00			16
		3 9 0 0 00				17
(e) 2 0 0 0 00		82 0 0 0 00				18
		8 0 0 0 00				19
		20 0 0 0 00				20
		3 0 0 0 00				21
(a)	(b)					22
151 0 0 0 00	139 5 0 0 00	151 0 0 0 00	139 5 0 0 00			23
(c) 3 0 0 00		3 0 0 00				24
(d) 6 0 0 00		6 0 0 00				25
	(e) 2 0 0 0 00				2 0 0 0 00	26
(f) 5 2 0 0 00		5 2 0 0 00				27
303 4 0 0 00	303 4 0 0 00	554 0 0 0 00	657 1 0 0 00	231 6 0 0 00	128 5 0 0 00	28
		103 1 0 0 00			103 1 0 0 00	29
		657 1 0 0 00	657 1 0 0 00	231 6 0 0 00	231 6 0 0 00	30
						31

NAME _____ DATE _____ CLASS _____

(For Problem 14-1A, see end of book.)

PROBLEM 14-2A or 14-2B

(The work sheet for this problem is at the end of the book.)

GENERAL JOURNAL   PAGE ___ *16*

	DATE	DESCRIPTION	POST. REF.	DEBIT	CREDIT	
1						1
2						2
3						3
4						4
5						5
6						6
7						7
8						8
9						9
10						10
11						11
12						12
13						13
14						14
15						15
16						16
17						17
18						18
19						19
20						20
21						21
22						22
23						23
24						24
25						25
26						26
27						27
28						28
29						29
30						30
31						31
32						32
33						33

PROBLEM 14-3A or 14-3B

	DATE	DESCRIPTION	POST. REF.	DEBIT	CREDIT	
1						1
2						2
3						3
4						4
5						5
6						6
7						7
8						8
9						9
10						10
11						11
12						12
13						13
14						14
15						15
16						16
17						17
18						18
19						19

PROBLEM 14-4A or 14-4B

(The work sheet for this problem is at the end of the book.)

GENERAL JOURNAL

	DATE	DESCRIPTION	POST. REF.	DEBIT	CREDIT	
1						1
2						2
3						3
4						4
5						5
6						6
7						7
8						8
9						9
10						10
11						11
12						12
13						13
14						14
15						15
16						16
17						17
18						18
19						19
20						20
21						21
22						22
23						23
24						24
25						25
26						26
27						27
28						28
29						29
30						30
31						31
32						32
33						33

APPENDIX C

PROBLEM C-1

PROBLEM C-2

PROBLEM C-3

15

Financial Statements and Closing Entries for a Merchandising Firm

LEARNING OBJECTIVES

1. Prepare a classified income statement for a merchandising firm.
2. Prepare a classified balance sheet for any type of business.
3. Compute working capital and current ratio.
4. Journalize the closing entries for a merchandising firm.
5. Determine which adjusting entries should be reversed, and journalize the reversing entries.

KEY TERMS

Cost of Goods Sold	Net income
Current assets	Net purchases
Current liabilities	Net sales
Current ratio	Notes receivable (current)
Delivered Cost of Purchases	Plant and equipment
General expenses	Reversing entries
Gross profit	Selling expenses
Liquidity	Temporary-equity accounts
Long-term liabilities	Working capital

STUDY GUIDE QUESTIONS

PART 1   True/False

For each of the following statements, circle T if the statement is true and F if the statement is false.

T   F   1. The cost of goods sold is obtained by subtracting the goods available for sale from the net sales.

T   F   2. An increase in Sales Returns and Allowances represents an increase in gross profit.

T   F   3. Gross profit is equal to net sales minus cost of goods sold.

T   F   4. Insurance Expense is classified in the Other Expenses section of an income statement.

T   F   5. Freight In is classified in the Operating Expenses section of an income statement.

T   F   6. In the Current Liabilities section of a balance sheet, Accounts Payable precedes Notes Payable.

T   F   7. An unearned revenue account is classified as a current liability.

T   F   8. Reversing entries are required for all adjusting entries.

T   F   9. In a balance sheet, Prepaid Insurance is classified in the Plant and Equipment section.

T   F   10. An increase in Rent Expense results in a decrease in gross profit.

PART 2   Completion—Language of Business

Complete each of the following statements by writing the appropriate word(s) in the spaces provided:

1. Current Assets minus Current Liabilities equals _____.
2. Net Sales minus Cost of Goods Sold is _____.
3. Goods Available for Sale minus ending Merchandise Inventory is called _____
    _____.
4. Gross Profit minus Operating Expenses is called _____.
5. Gross Purchases minus Purchases Returns and Allowances minus Purchases Discount
    plus _____ equals Delivered Cost of Purchases.

PART 3   Financial Statement Classifications

Classify the following accounts according to the title of the financial statement and the statement classification. The first two accounts are provided as examples.

Account Name	Financial Statement	Classification
0. Wages Expense	Income Statement	Operating Expenses
0. Accounts Payable	Balance Sheet	Current Liabilities
1. Purchases		
2. Accounts Receivable		
3. Building		
4. Freight In		
5. Interest Expense		
6. Supplies		
7. Sales Discount		
8. Unearned Subscriptions		
9. Accumulated Depreciation, Equipment		
10. Purchases Returns and Allowances		

DEMONSTRATION PROBLEM

Christy's Apparel has a fiscal year extending from January 1 through December 31. Its account balances after adjustments are presented below in random order. The beginning merchandise inventory amounts to $35,870. With regard to the outstanding mortgage, $2,000 is due within the next twelve months.

Notes Receivable	$ 7,000	Freight In	$ 7,040
Interest Income	5,362	Office Salary Expense	11,119
Building	45,400	Accounts Receivable	46,627
Accounts Payable	25,245	Store Supplies	1,094
Prepaid Insurance	1,090	Interest Expense	2,100
Insurance Expense	2,505	Cash	3,305
Accumulated Depreciation,		Depreciation Expense,	
Building	15,133	Office Equipment	1,775
Notes Payable	10,250	Purchases Discount	1,335
Sales	267,111	Accumulated Depreciation,	
Sales Salary Expense	60,377	Store Equipment	10,750
Rent Income	2,400	Salaries Payable	3,420
Store Equipment	21,500	C. P. Bennett, Drawing	60,000
Mortgage Payable (current portion		Office Equipment	8,875
is $2,000)	31,000	Taxes Expense	4,006
Land	10,000	Accumulated Depreciation,	
Sales Commission Expense	6,400	Office Equipment	4,438
Sales Discount	2,671	Miscellaneous General Expense	1,750
Merchandise Inventory,		Store Supplies Expense	1,918
Dec. 31, 19—	41,998	C. P. Bennett, Capital,	
Purchases	133,556	Jan. 1, 19—	110,980
Advertising Expense	5,342	Depreciation Expense, Building	1,297
Sales Returns and Allowances	3,149	Depreciation Expense,	
Purchases Returns and		Store Equipment	4,300
Allowances	2,642		

Instructions

1. Prepare a classified income statement and subdivide operating expenses.
2. Prepare a statement of owner's equity.
3. Prepare a balance sheet.
4. Determine the amount of working capital and the current ratio.

SOLUTION

1.

Christy's Apparel

Income Statement

For the Year Ended December 31, 19—

Revenue from Sales:			
Sales		$267 1 1 1 00	
Less: Sales Returns and Allowances	$ 3 1 4 9 00		
Sales Discount	2 6 7 1 00	5 8 2 0 00	
Net Sales			$261 2 9 1 00
Cost of Goods Sold:			
Merchandise Inventory, January 1, 19—		$ 35 8 7 0 00	
Purchases	$133 5 5 6 00		
Less: Purchases Returns and			
Allowances $2,642.00			
Purchases Discount 1,335.00	3 9 7 7 00		
Net Purchases	$129 5 7 9 00		
Add Freight In	7 0 4 0 00		
Delivered Cost of Purchases		136 6 1 9 00	
Goods Available for Sale		$172 4 8 9 00	
Less Merchandise Inventory,			
December 31, 19—		41 9 9 8 00	
Cost of Goods Sold			130 4 9 1 00
Gross Profit			$130 8 0 0 00
Operating Expenses:			
Selling Expenses:			
Sales Salary Expense	$ 60 3 7 7 00		
Sales Commission Expense	6 4 0 0 00		
Advertising Expense	5 3 4 2 00		
Depreciation Expense, Store Equipment	4 3 0 0 00		
Store Supplies Expense	1 9 1 8 00		
Total Selling Expenses		$ 78 3 3 7 00	
General Expenses:			
Office Salary Expense	$ 11 1 1 9 00		
Taxes Expense	4 0 0 6 00		
Depreciation Expense, Building	1 2 9 7 00		
Depreciation Expense, Office Equipment	1 7 7 5 00		
Insurance Expense	2 5 0 5 00		
Miscellaneous General Expense	1 7 5 0 00		
Total General Expenses		22 4 5 2 00	
Total Operating Expenses			100 7 8 9 00
Income from Operations			$ 30 0 1 1 00
Other Income:			
Rent Income		$ 2 4 0 0 00	
Interest Income		5 3 6 2 00	
Total Other Income		$ 7 7 6 2 00	
Other Expenses:			
Interest Expense		2 1 0 0 00	5 6 6 2 00
Net Income			$ 35 6 7 3 00

2.

Christy's Apparel

Statement of Owner's Equity

For the Year Ended December 31, 19—

C. P. Bennett, Capital, January 1, 19—			$110 980 00
Net Income for the Year	$35 673 00		
Less Withdrawals for the Year	60 000 00		
Decrease in Capital			24 327 00
C. P. Bennett, Capital, December 31, 19—			$ 86 653 00

3.

Christy's Apparel

Balance Sheet

December 31, 19—

Assets			
Current Assets:			
Cash	$ 3 305 00		
Notes Receivable	7 000 00		
Accounts Receivable	46 627 00		
Merchandise Inventory	41 998 00		
Store Supplies	1 094 00		
Prepaid Insurance	1 090 00		
Total Current Assets			$101 114 00
Plant and Equipment:			
Land	$10 000 00		
Building	$45 400 00		
Less Accumulated Depreciation	15 133 00	30 267 00	
Office Equipment	$ 8 875 00		
Less Accumulated Depreciation	4 438 00	4 437 00	
Store Equipment	$21 500 00		
Less Accumulated Depreciation	10 750 00	10 750 00	
Total Plant and Equipment			55 454 00
Total Assets			$156 568 00
Liabilities			
Current Liabilities:			
Notes Payable	$10 250 00		
Mortgage Payable (current portion)	2 000 00		
Accounts Payable	25 245 00		
Salaries Payable	3 420 00		
Total Current Liabilities		$40 915 00	
Long-Term Liabilities:			
Mortgage Payable		29 000 00	
Total Liabilities			$ 69 915 00
Owner's Equity			
C. P. Bennett, Capital			86 653 00
Total Liabilities and Owner's Equity			$156 568 00

4. Working capital = Current assets − Current liabilities

   = $101,114 − $40,915 = $60,199

   Current ratio = $\dfrac{\text{Current assets}}{\text{Current liabilities}}$ = $\dfrac{\$101,114}{\$40,915}$ = 2.47 : 1

NAME _____ DATE _____ CLASS _____

PROBLEM 15-1A or 15-1B

PROBLEM 15-1A or 15-1B (concluded)

GENERAL JOURNAL

	DATE	DESCRIPTION	POST. REF.	DEBIT	CREDIT	
1						1
2						2
3						3
4						4
5						5
6						6
7						7
8						8
9						9
10						10
11						11
12						12
13						13
14						14
15						15
16						16
17						17
18						18
19						19
20						20
21						21
22						22
23						23
24						24
25						25
26						26
27						27
28						28
29						29
30						30
31						31
32						32
33						33
34						34
35						35
36						36
37						37

PROBLEM 15-2A or 15-2B

PROBLEM 15-2A or 15-2B (continued)

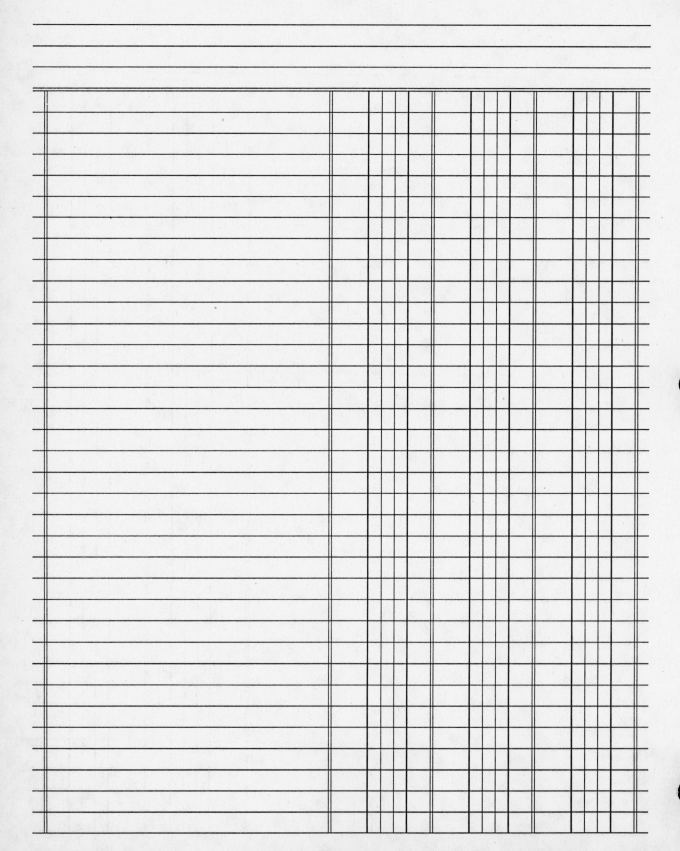

PROBLEM 15-2A or 15-2B (concluded)

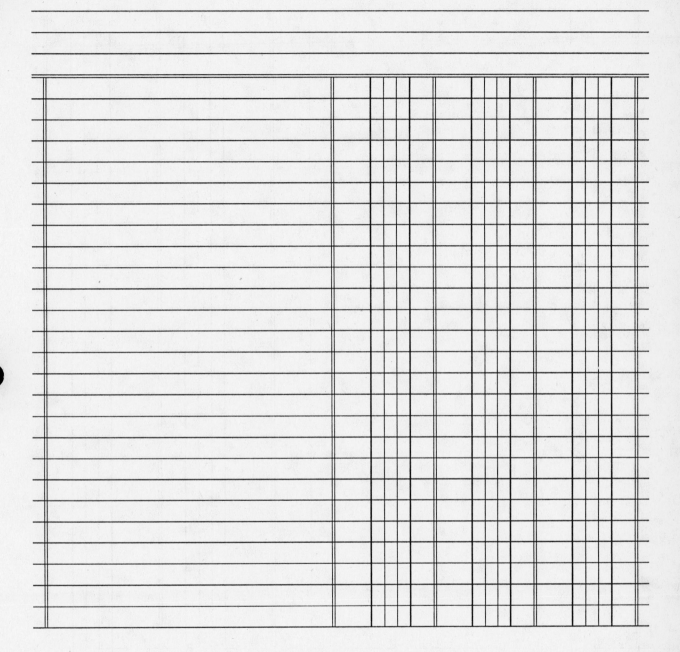

PROBLEM 15-3A or 15-3B

GENERAL JOURNAL

	DATE		DESCRIPTION	POST. REF.	DEBIT	CREDIT	
1							1
2							2
3							3
4							4
5							5
6							6
7							7
8							8
9							9
10							10
11							11
12							12
13							13
14							14
15							15
16							16
17							17
18							18
19							19
20							20
21							21
22							22
23							23
24							24
25							25
26							26
27							27
28							28
29							29
30							30
31							31
32							32
33							33
34							34
35							35
36							36
37							37

PROBLEM 15-3A or 15-3B (concluded)

GENERAL JOURNAL

	DATE	DESCRIPTION	POST. REF.	DEBIT	CREDIT	
1						1
2						2
3						3
4						4
5						5
6						6
7						7
8						8
9						9
10						10
11						11
12						12
13						13
14						14
15						15
16						16
17						17
18						18
19						19
20						20
21						21
22						22
23						23
24						24
25						25
26						26
27						27
28						28
29						29
30						30
31						31
32						32
33						33
34						34
35						35
36						36
37						37

PROBLEM 15-4A or 15-4B

(The work sheet for this problem is at the end of the book.)

PROBLEM 15-4A or 15-4B (continued)

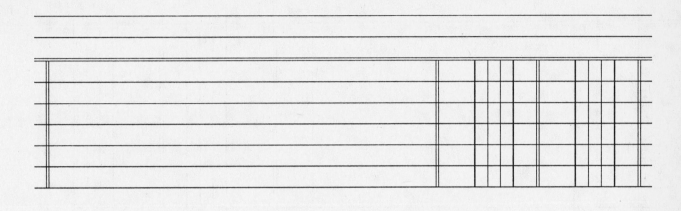

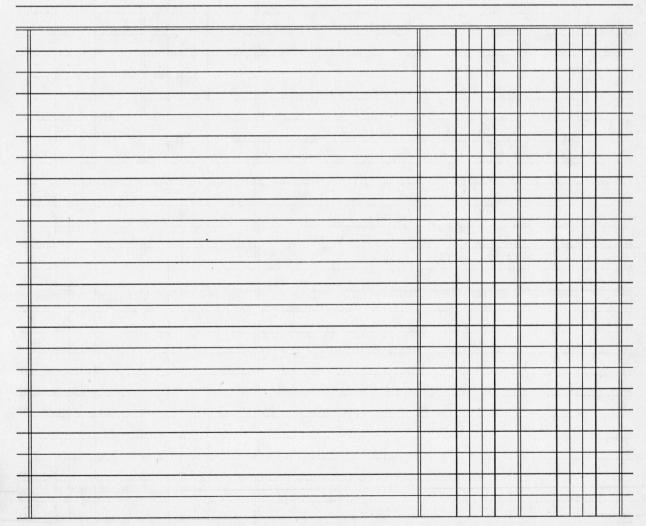

PROBLEM 15-4A or 15-4B (continued)

GENERAL JOURNAL

	DATE	DESCRIPTION	POST. REF.	DEBIT	CREDIT	
1						1
2						2
3						3
4						4
5						5
6						6
7						7
8						8
9						9
10						10
11						11
12						12
13						13
14						14
15						15
16						16
17						17
18						18
19						19
20						20
21						21
22						22
23						23
24						24
25						25
26						26
27						27
28						28
29						29
30						30
31						31
32						32
33						33
34						34
35						35
36						36
37						37

PROBLEM 15-4A or 15-4B (concluded)

GENERAL JOURNAL

PAGE _77__

	DATE	DESCRIPTION	POST. REF.	DEBIT	CREDIT	
1						1
2						2
3						3
4						4
5						5
6						6
7						7
8						8
9						9
10						10
11						11

a. Working Capital

b.   Current Ratio

APPENDIX D
PROBLEM D-1

APPENDIX D
PROBLEM D-2

APPENDIX D
PROBLEM D-3

APPENDIX E
PROBLEM E-1

a. Gross profit % (19x5) =

   Gross profit % (19x4) =

b. Net income % (19x5) =

   Net income % (19x4) =

PROBLEM E-2

Average merchandise inventory (19x5) =

Merchandise inventory turnover (19x5) =

Average merchandise inventory (19x4) =

Merchandise inventory turnover (19x4) =

PROBLEM E-3

Average capital (19x5) =

Return on investment (19x5) =

Average capital (19x4) =

Return on investment (19x4) =

COMPREHENSIVE REVIEW PROBLEM

SALES JOURNAL

	DATE	INV. NO.	CUSTOMER'S NAME	POST. REF.	ACCOUNTS RECEIVABLE DR., SALES CR.	
1						1
2						2
3						3
4						4
5						5
6						6
7						7

PURCHASES JOURNAL

	DATE	SUPPLIER'S NAME	INV. NO.	INV. DATE	TERMS	POST. REF.	ACCOUNTS PAYABLE CREDIT	FREIGHT IN DEBIT	PURCHASES DEBIT	
1										1
2										2
3										3
4										4
5										5
6										6
7										7

COMPREHENSIVE REVIEW PROBLEM (continued)

CASH RECEIPTS JOURNAL

PAGE 69

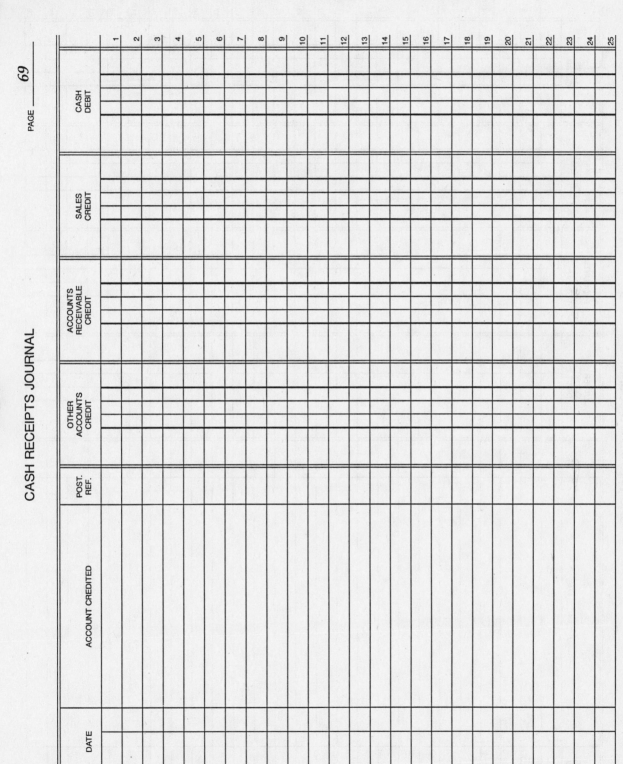

COMPREHENSIVE REVIEW PROBLEM (continued)

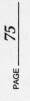

PAGE ___ 75

CASH PAYMENTS JOURNAL

		1	2	3	4	5	6	7	8	9	10	11	12	13	14	15	16	17	18	19	20	21	22	23	24	25	26
CASH CREDIT																											
PURCHASES DISCOUNT CREDIT																											
ACCOUNTS PAYABLE DEBIT																											
OTHER ACCOUNTS DEBIT																											
POST. REF.																											
ACCOUNT NAME																											
CK. NO.																											
DATE																											

COMPREHENSIVE REVIEW PROBLEM (continued)

GENERAL JOURNAL

PAGE ___*89*___

	DATE	DESCRIPTION	POST. REF.	DEBIT	CREDIT	
1						1
2						2
3						3
4						4
5						5
6						6
7						7
8						8
9						9
10						10
11						11
12						12
13						13
14						14
15						15
16						16
17						17
18						18
19						19
20						20
21						21
22						22
23						23
24						24
25						25
26						26
27						27
28						28
29						29
30						30
31						31
32						32
33						33
34						34
35						35
36						36
37						37

COMPREHENSIVE REVIEW PROBLEM (continued)

GENERAL JOURNAL

	DATE		DESCRIPTION	POST. REF.	DEBIT	CREDIT	
1							1
2							2
3							3
4							4
5							5
6							6
7							7
8							8
9							9
10							10
11							11
12							12
13							13
14							14
15							15

GENERAL JOURNAL

PAGE _____ 91

	DATE		DESCRIPTION	POST. REF.	DEBIT	CREDIT	
1							1
2							2
3							3
4							4
5							5
6							6
7							7
8							8
9							9
10							10
11							11
12							12
13							13
14							14
15							15
16							16
17							17
18							18
19							19

COMPREHENSIVE REVIEW PROBLEM (continued)

GENERAL JOURNAL

PAGE *92*

	DATE		DESCRIPTION	POST. REF.	DEBIT	CREDIT	
1							1
2							2
3							3
4							4
5							5
6							6
7							7
8							8
9							9
10							10
11							11
12							12
13							13
14							14
15							15
16							16
17							17
18							18
19							19
20							20
21							21
22							22
23							23
24							24
25							25
26							26
27							27
28							28
29							29
30							30
31							31
32							32
33							33
34							34
35							35
36							36
37							37

COMPREHENSIVE REVIEW PROBLEM (continued)

ACCOUNTS RECEIVABLE LEDGER

NAME *Brighton Hotel Corporation*

ADDRESS *4600 Beaumont Drive*

Houston, TX 77092

DATE	ITEM	POST. REF.	DEBIT	CREDIT	BALANCE

NAME *Burns and Taylor*

ADDRESS *1420 Favela Road*

Houston, TX 77091

DATE		ITEM	POST. REF.	DEBIT	CREDIT	BALANCE
19—						
Feb.	1	Balance	✓			11 6 1 9 50

NAME *Vargo Decorators*

ADDRESS *642 Guthrie St.*

Houston, TX 77090

DATE		ITEM	POST. REF.	DEBIT	CREDIT	BALANCE
19—						
Feb.	1	Balance	✓			4 9 2 0 14

COMPREHENSIVE REVIEW PROBLEM (continued)

ACCOUNTS PAYABLE LEDGER

NAME _J. P. Bryan, Inc._____

ADDRESS _400 W. Tatum St._____
Amarillo, TX 79177

DATE	ITEM	POST. REF.	DEBIT	CREDIT	BALANCE

NAME _Laurel Textiles_____

ADDRESS _1464 Harding Drive_____
Dallas, TX 75294

DATE		ITEM	POST. REF.	DEBIT	CREDIT	BALANCE
19—						
Feb.	1	Balance	√			17 6 2 4 10

NAME _Melnor Fabrics_____

ADDRESS _620 W. Huber St._____
Corpus Christi, TX 78487

DATE		ITEM	POST. REF.	DEBIT	CREDIT	BALANCE
19—						
Feb.	1	Balance	√			9 6 1 6 00

COMPREHENSIVE REVIEW PROBLEM (continued)

ACCOUNTS PAYABLE LEDGER

NAME _Sutton Manufacturing Company_____

ADDRESS _842 N. Howard Ave._____

_Fort Worth, TX 76196_____

DATE		ITEM	POST. REF.	DEBIT	CREDIT	BALANCE
19—						
Feb.	1	Balance	√			12 7 1 0 00

COMPREHENSIVE REVIEW PROBLEM (continued)

GENERAL LEDGER

ACCOUNT *Cash*   ACCOUNT NO. *111*

DATE	ITEM	POST. REF.	DEBIT	CREDIT	BALANCE DEBIT	BALANCE CREDIT
19—						
Feb. 1	Balance	✓			34 994 00	

ACCOUNT *Petty Cash Fund*   ACCOUNT NO. *113*

DATE	ITEM	POST. REF.	DEBIT	CREDIT	BALANCE DEBIT	BALANCE CREDIT
19—						
Feb.		✓			70 00	

ACCOUNT *Accounts Receivable*   ACCOUNT NO. *115*

DATE	ITEM	POST. REF.	DEBIT	CREDIT	BALANCE DEBIT	BALANCE CREDIT
19—						
Feb. 1	Balance	✓			16 539 64	

COMPREHENSIVE REVIEW PROBLEM (continued)

GENERAL LEDGER

ACCOUNT _Merchandise Inventory_ _____ ACCOUNT NO. _116_

DATE	ITEM	POST. REF.	DEBIT	CREDIT	BALANCE DEBIT	BALANCE CREDIT
19—						
Feb. 1	Balance	√			52 6 4 0 00	

ACCOUNT _Supplies_ _____ ACCOUNT NO. _117_

DATE	ITEM	POST. REF.	DEBIT	CREDIT	BALANCE DEBIT	BALANCE CREDIT
19—						
Feb. 1		√			5 1 6 50	

ACCOUNT _Prepaid Insurance_ _____ ACCOUNT NO. _118_

DATE	ITEM	POST. REF.	DEBIT	CREDIT	BALANCE DEBIT	BALANCE CREDIT
19—						
Feb. 1		√			4 8 0 00	

COMPREHENSIVE REVIEW PROBLEM (continued)

GENERAL LEDGER

ACCOUNT __Equipment__ _____ ACCOUNT NO. __121__

DATE	ITEM	POST. REF.	DEBIT	CREDIT	BALANCE DEBIT	BALANCE CREDIT
19—						
Feb. 1		√			9 3 2 4 00	

ACCOUNT __Accumulated Depreciation, Equipment__ _____ ACCOUNT NO. __122__

DATE	ITEM	POST. REF.	DEBIT	CREDIT	BALANCE DEBIT	BALANCE CREDIT
19—						
Feb. 1		√				5 3 2 8 00

ACCOUNT __Accounts Payable__ _____ ACCOUNT NO. __212__

DATE	ITEM	POST. REF.	DEBIT	CREDIT	BALANCE DEBIT	BALANCE CREDIT
19—						
Feb. 1	Balance	√				39 9 5 0 10

COMPREHENSIVE REVIEW PROBLEM (continued)

GENERAL LEDGER

ACCOUNT *Employees' Income Tax Payable* _____ ACCOUNT NO. _213_

DATE		ITEM	POST. REF.	DEBIT	CREDIT	BALANCE	
						DEBIT	CREDIT
19—							
Feb.	1	Balance	✓				1 3 9 1 60

ACCOUNT *FICA Tax Payable* _____ ACCOUNT NO. _214_

DATE		ITEM	POST. REF.	DEBIT	CREDIT	BALANCE	
						DEBIT	CREDIT
19—							
Feb.	1	Balance	✓				1 5 2 0 84

ACCOUNT *State Unemployment Tax Payable* _____ ACCOUNT NO. _215_

DATE		ITEM	POST. REF.	DEBIT	CREDIT	BALANCE	
						DEBIT	CREDIT
19—							
Feb.	1	Balance	✓				5 3 6 76

COMPREHENSIVE REVIEW PROBLEM (continued)

GENERAL LEDGER

ACCOUNT _Federal Unemployment Tax Payable_ _____ ACCOUNT NO. __216__

DATE	ITEM	POST. REF.	DEBIT	CREDIT	BALANCE DEBIT	BALANCE CREDIT
19—						
Feb. 1	Balance	✓				79 52

ACCOUNT _Salaries Payable_ _____ ACCOUNT NO. __219__

DATE	ITEM	POST. REF.	DEBIT	CREDIT	BALANCE DEBIT	BALANCE CREDIT
19—						
Feb. 1	Balance	✓				710 00

ACCOUNT _N. R. Bell, Capital_ _____ ACCOUNT NO. __311__

DATE	ITEM	POST. REF.	DEBIT	CREDIT	BALANCE DEBIT	BALANCE CREDIT
19—						
Feb. 1	Balance	✓				65 047 32

COMPREHENSIVE REVIEW PROBLEM (continued)

GENERAL LEDGER

ACCOUNT *N. R. Bell, Drawing*   ACCOUNT NO. *312*

DATE	ITEM	POST. REF.	DEBIT	CREDIT	BALANCE	
					DEBIT	CREDIT

ACCOUNT *Income Summary*   ACCOUNT NO. *313*

DATE	ITEM	POST. REF.	DEBIT	CREDIT	BALANCE	
					DEBIT	CREDIT

ACCOUNT *Sales*   ACCOUNT NO. *411*

DATE	ITEM	POST. REF.	DEBIT	CREDIT	BALANCE	
					DEBIT	CREDIT

COMPREHENSIVE REVIEW PROBLEM (continued)

GENERAL LEDGER

ACCOUNT *Sales Returns and Allowances*   ACCOUNT NO. *412*

DATE	ITEM	POST. REF.	DEBIT	CREDIT	BALANCE	
					DEBIT	CREDIT

ACCOUNT *Purchases*   ACCOUNT NO. *511*

DATE	ITEM	POST. REF.	DEBIT	CREDIT	BALANCE	
					DEBIT	CREDIT

ACCOUNT *Purchases Returns and Allowances*   ACCOUNT NO. *512*

DATE	ITEM	POST. REF.	DEBIT	CREDIT	BALANCE	
					DEBIT	CREDIT

ACCOUNT *Purchases Discount*   ACCOUNT NO. *513*

DATE	ITEM	POST. REF.	DEBIT	CREDIT	BALANCE	
					DEBIT	CREDIT

COMPREHENSIVE REVIEW PROBLEM (continued)

GENERAL LEDGER

ACCOUNT *Freight In*   ACCOUNT NO. *514*

DATE	ITEM	POST. REF.	DEBIT	CREDIT	BALANCE	
					DEBIT	CREDIT

ACCOUNT *Salary Expense*   ACCOUNT NO. *611*

DATE	ITEM	POST. REF.	DEBIT	CREDIT	BALANCE	
					DEBIT	CREDIT

ACCOUNT *Payroll Tax Expense*   ACCOUNT NO. *612*

DATE	ITEM	POST. REF.	DEBIT	CREDIT	BALANCE	
					DEBIT	CREDIT

COMPREHENSIVE REVIEW PROBLEM (continued)

GENERAL LEDGER

ACCOUNT *Rent Expense* ACCOUNT NO. *613*

DATE	ITEM	POST. REF.	DEBIT	CREDIT	BALANCE	
					DEBIT	CREDIT

ACCOUNT *Utilities Expense* ACCOUNT NO. *614*

DATE	ITEM	POST. REF.	DEBIT	CREDIT	BALANCE	
					DEBIT	CREDIT

ACCOUNT *Supplies Expense* ACCOUNT NO. *616*

DATE	ITEM	POST. REF.	DEBIT	CREDIT	BALANCE	
					DEBIT	CREDIT

COMPREHENSIVE REVIEW PROBLEM (continued)

GENERAL LEDGER

ACCOUNT *Insurance Expense* _____ ACCOUNT NO. *617*

DATE	ITEM	POST. REF.	DEBIT	CREDIT	BALANCE	
					DEBIT	CREDIT

ACCOUNT *Depreciation Expense, Equipment* _____ ACCOUNT NO. *618*

DATE	ITEM	POST. REF.	DEBIT	CREDIT	BALANCE	
					DEBIT	CREDIT

ACCOUNT *Miscellaneous Expense* _____ ACCOUNT NO. *619*

DATE	ITEM	POST. REF.	DEBIT	CREDIT	BALANCE	
					DEBIT	CREDIT

COMPREHENSIVE REVIEW PROBLEM (continued)

Bell Draperies

Schedule of Accounts Receivable

February 28, 19—

Bell Draperies

Schedule of Accounts Payable

February 28, 19—

COMPREHENSIVE REVIEW PROBLEM (continued)

Bell Draperies
Income Statement
For Month Ended February 28, 19—

COMPREHENSIVE REVIEW PROBLEM (continued)

Bell Draperies
Statement of Owner's Equity
For Month Ended February 28, 19—

COMPREHENSIVE REVIEW PROBLEM (continued)

Bell Draperies
Balance Sheet
February 28, 19—

COMPREHENSIVE REVIEW PROBLEM (concluded)

Bell Draperies

Post-Closing Trial Balance

February 28, 19—

ACCOUNT NAME	DEBIT	CREDIT
Cash		
Petty Cash Fund		
Accounts Receivable		
Merchandise Inventory		
Supplies		
Prepaid Insurance		
Equipment		
Accumulated Depreciation, Equipment		
Accounts Payable		
Employees' Income Tax Payable		
FICA Tax Payable		
State Unemployment Tax Payable		
Federal Unemployment Tax Payable		
Salaries Payable		
N. R. Bell, Capital		

Answers to Study Guide Questions

CHAPTER 1

PART 1   True/False

1. T   6. T
2. T   7. F
3. F   8. T
4. F   9. T
5. T   10. T

PART 2   Completion—Language of Business

1. sole proprietorship
2. liabilities
3. creditor
4. accounts
5. transaction
6. capital
7. fundamental accounting equation
8. chart of accounts
9. report
10. equity

PART 3   Classifying Accounts

Assets
Office Equipment
Supplies
Building
Cash
Land
Prepaid Insurance
Neon Sign

Liabilities
Accounts Payable
Mortgage Payable

Owner's Equity
R. D. Willard, Capital

PART 4   Completion—Balance Sheet

a. Niemi Insurance Agency
b. Balance Sheet
c. October 31, 19—
d. Assets
e. Total Assets
f. Liabilities
g. Owner's Equity
h. Total Liabilities and Owner's Equity
i. 127,772.00
j. 940.00
k. 69,832.00
l. 127,772.00

CHAPTER 2

PART 1   True/False

1. F   6. T
2. T   7. F
3. F   8. T
4. T   9. T
5. F   10. T

PART 2   Completion—Language of Business

1. Revenue
2. statement of owner's equity
3. withdrawal
4. net loss
5. fair market value
6. income statement
7. Accounts Receivable
8. Expenses

PART 3   Analyzing Transactions

	A	L	OE	R	E
0.	+		+		
1.	−				+
2.	+			+	
3.	+		+		
4.	+ −				
5.	−				+
6.	+			+	
7.	−		−		
8.	+	+			
9.	+ −				
10.	−	−			

PART 4   Statement of Owner's Equity

C. P. Sebring Company

Statement of Owner's Equity

For Month Ended June 30, 19—

C. P. Sebring, Capital, June 1, 19—			$106 5 0 0 00
Additional Investment, June 16, 19—			4 0 0 0 00
Total Investment			$110 5 0 0 00
Net Income for June	$3 4 0 0 00		
Less Withdrawals for June	3 2 0 0 00		
Increase in Capital			2 0 0 00
C. P. Sebring, Capital, June 30, 19—			$110 7 0 0 00

CHAPTER 3

PART 1 True/False

1.	F	6.	F
2.	T	7.	T
3.	T	8.	F
4.	F	9.	T
5.	F	10.	T

PART 2 Completion—Language of Business

1. debit
2. footings
3. transposition
4. trial balance
5. compound entry
6. credit

PART 3 Accounting Entries

Professional Equipment		Accounts Payable	
+	−	−	+
(a) 760		(a) 760	

Accounts Receivable		Professional Fees	
+	−	−	+
(b) 764		(b) 764	

Rent Expense		Cash	
+	−	+	−
(c) 950		(c) 950	

Supplies		Accounts Payable	
+	−	−	+
(d) 410		(d) 410	

Utilities Expense		Cash	
+	−	+	−
(e) 76		(e) 76	

Cash		Accounts Receivable	
+	−	+	−
(f) 610		(f) 610	

Accounts Payable		Cash	
−	+	+	−
(g) 500		(g) 500	

Salary Expense		Cash	
+	−	+	−
(h) 990		(h) 990	

Office Equipment		Cash	
+	−	+	−
(i) 342		(i) 342	

Accounts Payable		Supplies	
−	+	+	−
(j) 200		(j) 200	

CHAPTER 4

PART 1   True/False

1.	F	6.	T
2.	F	7.	F
3.	F	8.	F
4.	F	9.	T
5.	T	10.	F

PART 2   Completion—Language of Business

1. chart of accounts
2. posting
3. source documents
4. cost principle
5. journalizing
6. Posting Reference column of the journal
7. account numbers

PART 3   Completing a Journal Entry

GENERAL JOURNAL

PAGE __33__

	DATE		DESCRIPTION	POST. REF.	DEBIT	CREDIT	
1	19—						1
2	Oct.	29	Cash	111	1 1 0 0 00		2
3			Accounts Receivable	113	6 0 0 00		3
4			Income from Services	411		1 7 0 0 00	4
5			Received partial payment for				5
6			services performed.				6
7							7
8							8

1. $600 ($1,700 − $1,100)
2. $2,800 ($600 + $1,100 + $1,100)
3. $1,300 ($700 + $400 + $200)
4. compound

CHAPTER 5

PART 1   True/False

1.	F	6.	T
2.	T	7.	T
3.	T	8.	T
4.	F	9.	F
5.	F	10.	T

PART 2   Completion—Language of Business

1.	book value	6.	accounting cycle
2.	fiscal period	7.	mixed accounts
3.	contra	8.	matching principle
4.	adjustments	9.	depreciation
5.	accrued wages		

PART 3   Adjusting Entries

1.

Prepaid Insurance				Insurance Expense	
Bal.	830	Adj.	420	Adj.	420

2.

Supplies				Supplies Expense	
Bal.	980	Adj.	340	Adj.	340

3.

Accumulated Depreciation, Equipment				Depreciation Expense, Equipment	
		Bal.	4,100	Adj.	2,000
		Adj.	2,000		

4.

Wages Expense				Wages Payable	
Bal.	7,200			Adj.	330
Adj.	330				

PART 4 Analyzing the Work Sheet

Account Name	Trial Balance Debit	Trial Balance Credit	Adjustments Debit	Adjustments Credit	Adj. Trial Balance Debit	Adj. Trial Balance Credit	Income Statement Debit	Income Statement Credit	Balance Sheet Debit	Balance Sheet Credit
0. Equipment	X				X				X	
0. Supplies Expense			X		X		X			
1. Cash	X				X				X	
2. C. Dahl, Capital		X				X				X
3. Advertising Expense	X				X		X			
4. Accounts Receivable	X				X				X	
5. Wages Expense	X		X		X		X			
6. Accumulated Depreciation, Equipment		X		X		X				X
7. Wages Payable				X		X				X
8. Supplies	X			X	X				X	
9. C. Dahl, Drawing	X				X				X	
10. Service Revenue		X				X		X		

CHAPTER 6

PART 1 True/False

1.	F	6.	F
2.	T	7.	T
3.	T	8.	F
4.	F	9.	T
5.	F	10.	T

PART 2 Completion—Language of Business

1. post-closing trial balance
2. real or permanent
3. interim
4. Income Summary
5. closing entry
6. nominal or temporary-equity
7. accrual basis
8. modified cash basis

PART 3 Closing Entries

	Debit	Credit
1.	b	d
2.	d	a, f
3.	d	e
4.	e	c

PART 4 Posting Closing Entries

1. $41,000
2. $46,000
3. $ 5,000 net loss ($6,000 − $41,000)
4. $22,000

5. J. See, Capital; Income Summary
6. J. See, Capital; J. See, Drawing
7. $27,000 decrease ($22,000 + $5,000 net loss)
8. $123,000 ($150,000 − $22,000 − $5,000)

CHAPTER 7

PART 1 True/False

1. T   6. T
2. T   7. F
3. F   8. T
4. F   9. F
5. T   10. T

PART 2 Chart of Accounts

Assets
Cash
Accounts Receivable
Supplies
Prepaid Insurance
Office Equipment
Accumulated Depreciation,
    Office Equipment

Liabilities
Deposits Payable
Accounts Payable

Owner's Equity
C. C. Pietro, Capital
C. C. Pietro, Drawing
Income Summary

Revenue
Commissions Income

Expenses
Salary Expense
Advertising Expense
Automobile Expense
Rent Expense
Telephone Expense
Utilities Expense
Supplies Expense
Insurance Expense
Depreciation Expense,
    Office Equipment
Miscellaneous Expense

PART 3 Combined Journal

Cash Debit, Cash Credit
Other Accounts Debit, Other Accounts Credit
Accounts Receivable Debit, Accounts Receivable Credit
Deposits Payable Debit, Deposits Payable Credit
C. C. Pietro, Drawing, Debit
Commissions Income Credit
Advertising Expense Debit
Salary Expense Debit
Automobile Expense Debit

CHAPTER 8

PART 1   True/False

1.	F	6.	T
2.	F	7.	T
3.	F	8.	F
4.	F	9.	F
5.	T	10.	F

PART 2   Completion—Language of Business

1. payee
2. service charge
3. endorsement
4. denominations
5. canceled checks
6. restrictive endorsement
7. drawer
8. ledger balance of cash
9. deposit in transit
10. change fund
11. qualified endorsement
12. bank reconciliation
13. Outstanding checks
14. blank endorsement

PART 3   Reimbursing the Petty Cash Fund

Balance of the Petty Cash Fund, $60

GENERAL JOURNAL   PAGE _____

	DATE		DESCRIPTION	POST. REF.	DEBIT			CREDIT			
1	19—										1
2	June	30	Repair Expense			7	10				2
3			Delivery Expense			4	20				3
4			Miscellaneous Expense		1	6	48				4
5			H. Ball, Drawing		1	1	50				5
6			Cash					3	9	28	6
7			Issued Ck. No. 711 to reimburse								7
8			the petty cash fund.								8
9											9
10											10
11											11
12											12
13											13

CHAPTER 9

PART 1   True/False

1.	T	6.	F
2.	F	7.	T
3.	F	8.	F
4.	F	9.	T
5.	T	10.	F

PART 2   Completion—Language of Business

1. gross pay
2. employee
3. exemption
4. net pay
5. independent contractor
6. employee's individual earnings record

PART 3   Calculation of Earnings

Employee's Name	Hours Worked	Regular Hourly Rate	Total Earnings
A.L. Gonzales	42	$ 9.60	$412.80
L.A. Lamar	46	8.40	411.60
C.W. Nelson	51	10.20	576.30

PART 4   Payroll Entry

GENERAL JOURNAL   PAGE ___79___

	DATE		DESCRIPTION	POST. REF.	DEBIT	CREDIT	
1	19—						1
2	Mar.	14	Sales Salary Expense		72 0 0 0 00		2
3			Office Salary Expense		21 6 4 0 00		3
4			Employees' Fed. Income Tax Pay.			9 3 0 0 00	4
5			FICA Tax Payable			7 1 6 3 46	5
6			Employees' Bond Deductions Pay.			9 0 0 00	6
7			Employees' Union Dues Payable			1 2 0 0 00	7
8			Employees' Medical Insurance Pay.			2 0 0 0 00	8
9			Salaries Payable			73 0 7 6 54	9
10			To record payroll for the week				10
11			ended March 14.				11
12							12

CHAPTER 10

PART 1   True/False

1. F		6. T	
2. F		7. F	
3. T		8. T	
4. F		9. T	
5. T		10. F	

PART 2   Completion—Language of Business

1. quarter
2. Form W-2
3. employer identification number
4. Payroll Tax Expense
5. Workers' compensation insurance
6. Form W-3
7. Form 941

PART 3 Completing Form W-2

1 Control number	22222	For Official Use Only ► OMB No. 1545-0008		

2 Employer's name, address, and ZIP code	6 Statutory employee ☐ Deceased ☐ Pension plan ☐ Legal rep. ☐ 942 emp. ☐ Subtotal ☐ Deferred compensation ☐ Void ☐	
Barclay Company 1620 Hampton Place Boston, MA 02116	7 Allocated tips 0	8 Advance EIC payment 0
	9 Federal income tax withheld 3,716.22	10 Wages, tips, other compensation 34,218.42

3 Employer's identification number 72-1162127	4 Employer's state I.D. number 42-6916	11 Social security tax withheld 2,121.54	12 Social security wages 34,218.42
5 Employee's social security number 561-24-5229		13 Social security tips 0	14 Medicare wages and tips 34,218.42

19a Employee's name (first, middle, last) June Clara Perkins	15 Medicare tax withheld 496.67	16 Nonqualified plans
2219 Henderson Street Boston, MA 02121	17 See Instrs. for Form W-2	18 Other 0
19b Employee's address and ZIP code		

20	21	22 Dependent care benefits	23 Benefits included in Box 10

24 State income tax 1,780.04	25 State wages, tips, etc. 34,218.42	26 Name of state MA	27 Local income tax	28 Local wages, tips, etc.	29 Name of locality

Copy A For Social Security Administration

Department of the Treasury—Internal Revenue Service

Form W-2 Wage and Tax Statement

For Paperwork Reduction Act Notice, see separate instructions.

Form **940**

Department of the Treasury
Internal Revenue Service

Employer's Annual Federal Unemployment (FUTA) Tax Return

▶ For Paperwork Reduction Act Notice, see page 2.

OMB No 1545-0028

T	
FF	
FD	
FP	
I	
T	

If incorrect, make any necessary change. ▶

Name (as distinguished from trade name)

Calendar year 19—

Trade name, if any

Millard and Company

Address and ZIP code

820 Starbuck Road
Nelson, WY 82894

Employer identification number 29-5229364

A Did you pay all required contributions to state unemployment funds by the due date of Form 940? (See instructions if none required.) ☒ Yes ☐ No

If you checked the "Yes" box, enter the amount of contributions paid to state unemployment funds ▶ $ 1,134.00

B Are you required to pay contributions to only one state? ☒ Yes ☐ No

If you checked the "Yes" box: (1) Enter the name of the state where you are required to pay contributions ▶ Wyoming

(2) Enter your state reporting number(s) as shown on state unemployment tax return. ▶ 367-514

C If any part of wages taxable for FUTA tax is exempt from state unemployment tax, check the box. (See the Specific Instructions on page 4.) ☐

Note: *If you checked the "Yes" boxes in both questions A and B and did not check the box in C above, you may be able to use Form 940-EZ.*

If you will not have to file returns in the future, write "Final" here (see general instruction "Who Must File") and sign the return. ▶

Part I Computation of Taxable Wages (to be completed by all taxpayers)

		Amount paid		
1	Total payments (including exempt payments) during the calendar year for services of employees		1	93,700 00
2	Exempt payments. (Explain each exemption shown, attaching additional sheets if necessary.) ▶	2		
3	Payments for services of more than $7,000. Enter only the excess over the first $7,000 paid to individual employees not including exempt amounts shown on line 2. Do not use the state wage limitation.	3 72,700 00		
4	Total exempt payments (add lines 2 and 3)		4	72,700 00
5	**Total taxable wages** (subtract line 4 from line 1). (If any part is exempt from state contributions, see instructions.) ▶		5	21,000 00

Part II Tax Due or Refund (Complete if you checked the "Yes" boxes in both questions A and B and did not check the box in C above.)

1	**Total FUTA tax.** Multiply the wages in Part I, line 5, by .008 and enter here	1	168 00
2	Total FUTA tax deposited for the year, including any overpayment applied from a prior year (from your records)	2	161 36
3	**Balance due** (subtract line 2 from line 1). This should be $100 or less. Pay to IRS ▶	3	6 64
4	**Overpayment** (subtract line 1 from line 2). Check if it is to be: ☐ Applied to next return, or ☐ Refunded ▶	4	

Part III Tax Due or Refund (Complete if you checked the "No" box in either question A or B or you checked the box in C above. Also complete Part V.)

1	Gross FUTA tax. Multiply the wages in Part I, line 5, by .062		1	
2	Maximum credit. Multiply the wages in Part I, line 5, by .054	2		
3	**Credit allowable:** Enter the smaller of the amount in Part V, line 11, or Part III, line 2	3		
4	**Total FUTA tax** (subtract line 3 from line 1)		4	
5	Total FUTA tax deposited for the year, including any overpayment applied from a prior year (from your records)		5	
6	**Balance due** (subtract line 5 from line 4). This should be $100 or less. Pay to IRS ▶		6	
7	**Overpayment** (subtract line 4 from line 5). Check if it is to be: ☐ Applied to next return, or ☐ Refunded ▶		7	

Part IV Record of Quarterly Federal Tax Liability for Unemployment Tax (Do not include state liability.)

Quarter	First	Second	Third	Fourth	Total for Year
Liability for quarter	161.36	6.64	0	0	168.00

Part V Computation of Tentative Credit (Complete if you checked the "No" box in either question A or B or you checked the box in C above—see instructions.)

Name of state 1	State reporting number(s) as shown on employer's state contribution returns 2	Taxable payroll (as defined in state act) 3	State experience rate period 4 From—	To—	State experience rate 5	Contributions if rate had been 5.4% (col. 3 x .054) 6	Contributions payable at experience rate (col 3 x col 5) 7	Additional credit (col 6 minus col 7) If 0 or less, enter 0 8	Contributions actually paid to the state 9
WY	367-514	21,000	Jan. 1	Dec. 31	5.4	1,134	1,134	0	1,134
10 Totals ▶		21,000						0	1,134

11 Total tentative credit (add line 10, columns 8 and 9 only—see instructions for limitations) ▶ 1,134 00

Under penalties of perjury, I declare that I have examined this return, including accompanying schedules and statements, and to the best of my knowledge and belief, it is true, correct, and complete, and that no part of any payment made to a state unemployment fund claimed as a credit was or is to be deducted from the payments to employees

Signature ▶ C. N. Millard Title (Owner, etc.) ▶ Owner Date ▶ 1/30/—

Form **940**

CHAPTER 11

PART 1   True/False

1.	T	6.	F
2.	F	7.	F
3.	T	8.	T
4.	F	9.	F
5.	F	10.	T

PART 2   Completion—Language of Business

1. sales journal
2. merchandise inventory
3. special journals
4. controlling account
5. subsidiary ledger
6. credit memorandum
7. summarizing entry

PART 3   Posting

SALES JOURNAL

PAGE 26

DATE		INV. NO.	CUSTOMER'S NAME	POST. REF.	ACCOUNTS RECEIVABLE DEBIT	SALES TAX PAYABLE CREDIT	SALES CREDIT
19—							
June	1	32	Calvin Parsons		1 4 5 60	5 60	1 4 0 00
	30	171	Clara Lambert		1 6 1 41	6 21	1 5 5 20
	30				3 1 6 8 07	1 2 1 85	3 0 4 6 22
					(1 1 3)	(2 1 4)	(4 1 1)

GENERAL LEDGER

ACCOUNT Accounts Receivable   ACCOUNT NO. 113

DATE		ITEM	POST. REF.	DEBIT	CREDIT	BALANCE DEBIT	BALANCE CREDIT
19—							
June	30		S26	3 1 6 8 07		3 1 6 8 07	

ACCOUNT Sales Tax Payable   ACCOUNT NO. 214

DATE		ITEM	POST. REF.	DEBIT	CREDIT	BALANCE DEBIT	BALANCE CREDIT
19—							
June	30		S26		1 2 1 85		1 2 1 85

DATE		ITEM	POST. REF.	DEBIT	CREDIT	BALANCE	
						DEBIT	CREDIT
19—							
June	30		S26		3046 22		3046 22

CHAPTER 12

PART 1　True/False

1. F　　6. F
2. T　　7. F
3. F　　8. T
4. T　　9. T
5. F　　10. T

PART 2　Completion—Language of Business

1. Freight In
2. purchase order
3. FOB shipping point
4. internal control
5. crossfooting
6. purchase invoice
7. credit memorandum
8. FOB destination

CHAPTER 13

PART 1　True/False

1. T　　6. F
2. F　　7. F
3. F　　8. T
4. T　　9. T
5. F　　10. T

PART 2　Completion—Language of Business

1. trade discounts
2. credit period
3. cash discount

PART 3　Matching

1. P　　6. J
2. CR　　7. J
3. J　　8. CP
4. CR　　9. S
5. J　　10. CP

PART 4   Cash Receipts Journal

Other Accounts Credit
Accounts Receivable Credit
Sales Credit
Sales Discount Debit
Cash Debit

CHAPTER 14

PART 1   True/False

1. T	6. T
2. F	7. T
3. F	8. F
4. F	9. T
5. T	10. F

PART 2   Identifying Work Sheet Columns

Account Name	Income Statement		Balance Sheet	
	Debit	Credit	Debit	Credit
Example: 0. Rent Income		✓		
1. Sales Discount	✓			
2. C. Carr, Drawing			✓	
3. Supplies Expense	✓			
4. Sales		✓		
5. Merchandise Inventory			✓	
6. Purchases Returns and Allowances		✓		
7. Income Summary	✓	✓		
8. C. Carr, Capital				✓
9. Accumulated Depreciation, Equipment				✓
10. Purchases	✓			
11. Sales Returns and Allowances	✓			
12. Purchases Discount		✓		
13. Unearned Rent				✓
14. Supplies			✓	
15. Salaries Payable				✓

CHAPTER 15

PART 1   True/False

1.	F	6.	F
2.	F	7.	T
3.	T	8.	F
4.	F	9.	F
5.	F	10.	F

PART 2   Completion—Language of Business

1. working capital
2. gross profit
3. Cost of Goods Sold
4. Income from Operations
5. Freight In

PART 3   Financial Statement Classifications

Account Name	Financial Statement	Classification
0. Wages Expense	Income Statement	Operating Expenses
0. Accounts Payable	Balance Sheet	Current Liabilities
1. Purchases	Income Statement	Cost of Goods Sold
2. Accounts Receivable	Balance Sheet	Current Assets
3. Building	Balance Sheet	Plant and Equipment
4. Freight In	Income Statement	Cost of Goods Sold
5. Interest Expense	Income Statement	Other Expenses
6. Supplies	Balance Sheet	Current Assets
7. Sales Discount	Income Statement	Revenue from Sales
8. Unearned Subscriptions	Balance Sheet	Current Liabilities
9. Accumulated Depreciation, Equipment	Balance Sheet	Plant and Equipment
10. Purchases Returns and Allowances	Income Statement	Cost of Goods Sold

CHECK FIGURES FOR PROBLEMS

Problem	Check Figure
1-1A	Cash, $20,620
1-2A	Total assets, $66,770
1-3A	Cash, $11,937
1-4A	Capital, $51,722
1-1B	Cash, $4,250
1-2B	Total assets, $171,240
1-3B	Cash, $12,698
1-4B	Capital, $22,229
2-1A	Cash, $9,704
2-2A	Cash, $13,813
2-3A	Net income, $3,089
2-4A	Cash, $4,077
2-1B	Cash, $18,778
2-2B	Cash, $22,406
2-3B	Net income, $3,126
2-4B	Cash, $9,502
3-1A	Cash, $19,435
3-2A	Trial balance total, $28,925
3-3A	Net income, $3,950
3-4A	Net loss, $200
3-1B	Cash, $20,592
3-2B	Trial balance total, $26,796
3-3B	Net income, $3,490
3-4B	Net income, $24
4-2A	Trial balance total, $52,836
4-3A	Trial balance total, $25,604.65
4-4A	Trial balance total, $34,485.40
4-2B	Trial balance total, $52,936
4-3B	Trial balance total, $26,231.45
4-4B	Trial balance total, $6,401
5-1A	Net income, $3,002
5-2A	Total assets, $9,537
5-3A	Net income, $4,700
5-4A	Net income, $8,925
5-1B	Net income, $1,368
5-2B	Total assets, $10,889
5-3B	Net income, $9,732
5-4B	Net income, $12,672
6-1A	Ending capital, $45,114
6-2A	Ending balance of capital, $33,021
6-3A	Post-closing trial balance total, $14,206
6-4A	Ending Capital, $12,703.50
6-1B	Ending Capital, $40,513
6-2B	Ending balance of capital, $25,110
6-3B	Post-closing trial balance total, $22,122
6-4B	Ending capital, $9,135

Problem	Check Figure
Accounting Cycle Review Problem	
	Trial balance total, $615,642.50
	Net income, $15,122.16
7-1A	Total debits, $27,414.75
7-2A	Total Other Accounts Debit column, $173,211.40
7-3A	Total debits, $13,157.77
7-4A	Total debits, $128,977
7-1B	Total debits, $27,480.35
7-2B	Total Other Accounts Debit column, $150,045.40
7-3B	Total debits, $12,033
7-4B	Total debits, $50,305
8-1A	Adjusted Bank Statement Balance, $3,788.50
8-2A	Payments, $85.70
8-3A	Cash overage on June 30, $1.75
8-4A	Adjusted Bank Statement Balance, $3,666.00
8-1B	Adjusted Bank Statement Balance, $4,079.52
8-2B	Payments, $78.65
8-3B	Cash shortage on May 3, $1.25
8-4B	Adjusted Bank Statement Balance, $4,192.08
9-1A	Net pay, $344.01
9-2A	Net Amount, $1,684.42
9-3A	Net Amount, $2,628.70
9-4A	Net Amount, $4,789.31
9-1B	Net pay, $414.42
9-2B	Net Amount, $1,626.70
9-3B	Net Amount, $2,635.23
9-4B	Net Amount, $4,650.67
10-1A	Payroll tax expense, $937.37
10-2A	Payroll tax expense, $255.49
10-3A	Total taxes, $9,864.31
10-4A	Payroll tax expense, $1,190.54
10-1B	Payroll tax expense, $800.48
10-2B	Payroll tax expense, $272.13
10-3B	Total taxes, $9,005.46
10-4B	Payroll tax expense, $1,544.83
11-1A	Sales, $9,089.26 credit balance
11-2A	Accounts Receivable, $5,678.19 debit balance
11-3A	Accounts Receivable, $722.45 debit balance
11-4A	Sales, $39,763 credit balance

Problem	Check Figure	Problem	Check Figure
11-1B	Sales, $9,193.45 credit balance	13-1B	Cash Debit total, $85,687.54
11-2B	Accounts Receivable, $5,891.65 debit balance	13-2B	Cash Debit total, $25,719.00
11-3B	Accounts Receivable, $645.90 debit balance	13-3B	First National Bank Credit, $9,395.40
11-4B	Sales, $41,269 credit balance	13-4B	Cash Debit balance, $22,196.14
			Trial balance total, $90,410.80
12-1A	Accounts Payable, $50,471.49	14-1A	Net income, $44,774.50
12-2A	Accounts Payable, $14,294.18	14-2A	Net income, $53,193.00
12-3A	Total sales, $12,014.86	14-3A	Net income, $32,904.64
12-4A	Accounts Payable, $6,522.50	14-4A	Net income, $62,060.00
12-1B	Accounts Payable, $9,183.96	14-1B	Net income, $40,074.08
12-2B	Accounts Payable, $12,218.85	14-2B	Net income, $47,390.00
12-3B	Total sales, $23,995.56	14-3B	Net income, $54,170.00
12-4B	Accounts Payable, $6,651.00	14-4B	Net income, $48,000.00
13-1A	Cash Debit, $52,825.43	15-1A	Income from Operations, $56,989.60
13-2A	Cash Debit, $15,305.68	15-2A	Total Assets, $539,219.52
13-3A	First National Bank Credit, $6,051.64	15-3A	Amount of reversing entry, $1,022.40
		15-4A	Net Loss, $2,943.06
13-4A	Cash Debit balance, $23,812.18	15-1B	Income from Operations, $5,220.00
	Trial balance total, $94,112.46	15-2B	Total Assets, $262,036.80
		15-3B	Amount of reversing entry, $1,488
		15-4B	Net Loss, $10,182.00

PROBLEM

GENERAL JOURNAL

	DATE		DESCRIPTION	POST. REF.	DEBIT	CREDIT	
1							1
2							2
3							3
4							4
5							5
6							6
7							7
8							8
9							9
10							10
11							11
12							12
13							13
14							14
15							15
16							16
17							17
18							18
19							19
20							20
21							21
22							22
23							23
24							24
25							25
26							26
27							27
28							28
29							29
30							30
31							31
32							32
33							33
34							34
35							35
36							36
37							37

PROBLEM

GENERAL LEDGER

ACCOUNT _____ ACCOUNT NO. _____

DATE	ITEM	POST. REF.	DEBIT	CREDIT	BALANCE	
					DEBIT	CREDIT

PROBLEM

GENERAL LEDGER

ACCOUNT _____ ACCOUNT NO. _____

DATE	ITEM	POST. REF.	DEBIT	CREDIT	BALANCE	
					DEBIT	CREDIT

ACCOUNT _____ ACCOUNT NO. _____

DATE	ITEM	POST. REF.	DEBIT	CREDIT	BALANCE	
					DEBIT	CREDIT

ACCOUNT _____ ACCOUNT NO. _____

DATE	ITEM	POST. REF.	DEBIT	CREDIT	BALANCE	
					DEBIT	CREDIT

PROBLEM

NAME _____

ADDRESS _____

_____

DATE	ITEM	POST. REF.	DEBIT	CREDIT	BALANCE

PROBLEM

NAME _____

ADDRESS _____

_____

	DATE	ITEM	POST. REF.	DEBIT	CREDIT	BALANCE

NAME _____

ADDRESS _____

_____

	DATE	ITEM	POST. REF.	DEBIT	CREDIT	BALANCE

NAME _____

ADDRESS _____

_____

	DATE	ITEM	POST. REF.	DEBIT	CREDIT	BALANCE

PROBLEM

ACCOUNT NAME	DEBIT	CREDIT

NAME _____ DATE _____ CLASS _____

PROBLEM

NAME _____ DATE _____ CLASS _____

PROBLEM

NAME _____ DATE _____ CLASS _____

PROBLEM

NAME _____ DATE _____ CLASS _____

● PROBLEM

_____

_____
_____
_____

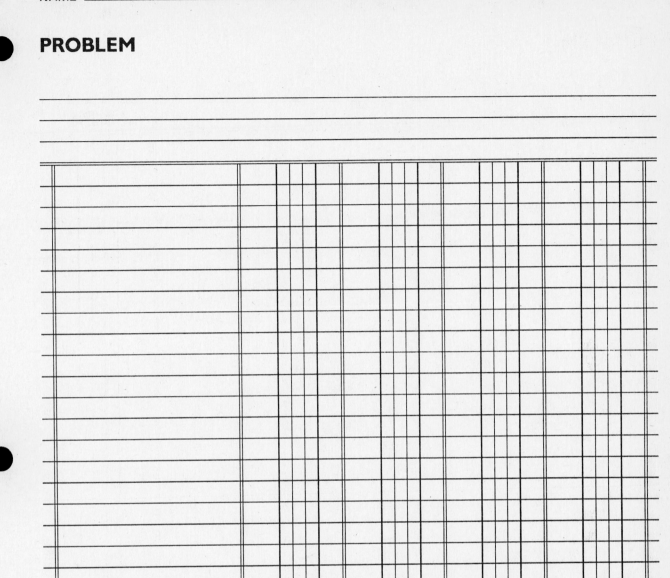

PROBLEM

SALES JOURNAL

	DATE	INV. NO.	CUSTOMER'S NAME	POST. REF.	ACCOUNTS RECEIVABLE DR., SALES CR.	
1						1
2						2
3						3
4						4
5						5
6						6
7						7
8						8
9						9
10						10
11						11
12						12
13						13
14						14
15						15
16						16
17						17
18						18
19						19
20						20
21						21
22						22
23						23
24						24
25						25
26						26
27						27
28						28
29						29
30						30
31						31
32						32
33						33
34						34
35						35
36						36

PROBLEM

SALES JOURNAL

PAGE _____

	DATE	INV. NO.	CUSTOMER'S NAME	POST. REF.	ACCOUNTS RECEIVABLE DEBIT	SALES TAX PAYABLE CREDIT	SALES CREDIT	
1								1
2								2
3								3
4								4
5								5
6								6
7								7
8								8
9								9
10								10
11								11
12								12
13								13
14								14
15								15
16								16
17								17
18								18
19								19
20								20
21								21
22								22
23								23
24								24
25								25
26								26
27								27
28								28
29								29
30								30
31								31
32								32
33								33
34								34
35								35
36								36

PROBLEM

PURCHASES JOURNAL

PAGE _____

	DATE		SUPPLIER'S NAME	INV. NO.	INV. DATE	TERMS	POST. REF.	ACCOUNTS PAYABLE CREDIT	FREIGHT IN DEBIT	PURCHASES DEBIT	
1											1
2											2
3											3
4											4
5											5
6											6
7											7
8											8
9											9
10											10
11											11
12											12
13											13
14											14
15											15
16											16
17											17
18											18
19											19
20											20
21											21
22											22
23											23
24											24
25											25
26											26
27											27
28											28
29											29
30											30
31											31
32											32
33											33
34											34
35											35
36											36

PROBLEM

PURCHASES JOURNAL

PAGE _____

DATE	SUPPLIER'S NAME	INVOICE NUMBER	INVOICE DATE	TERMS	POST. REF.	ACCOUNTS PAYABLE CREDIT	PURCHASES DEBIT	FREIGHT IN DEBIT	OTHER ACCOUNTS DEBIT		
									ACCOUNT	POST. REF.	AMOUNT

PROBLEM

CASH RECEIPTS JOURNAL

	CASH DEBIT	SALES DISCOUNT DEBIT	SALES CREDIT	ACCOUNTS RECEIVABLE CREDIT	OTHER ACCOUNTS CREDIT	POST. REF.	ACCOUNT CREDITED	DATE
1								
2								
3								
4								
5								
6								
7								
8								
9								
10								
11								
12								
13								
14								
15								
16								
17								
18								
19								
20								
21								
22								
23								
24								
25								
26								

PROBLEM

CASH PAYMENTS JOURNAL

		1	2	3	4	5	6	7	8	9	10	11	12	13	14	15	16	17	18	19	20	21	22	23	24	25	26
CASH CREDIT																											
PURCHASES DISCOUNT CREDIT																											
ACCOUNTS PAYABLE DEBIT																											
OTHER ACCOUNTS DEBIT																											
POST. REF.																											
ACCOUNT NAME																											
CK. NO.																											
DATE		1	2	3	4	5	6	7	8	9	10	11	12	13	14	15	16	17	18	19	20	21	22	23	24	25	26

PROBLEM

CASH PAYMENTS JOURNAL

PAGE _____

DATE	CK. NO.	ACCOUNT NAME	POST. REF.	OTHER ACCOUNTS DEBIT	ACCOUNTS PAYABLE DEBIT	PURCHASES DISCOUNT CREDIT	CASH CREDIT
1							
2							
3							
4							
5							
6							
7							
8							
9							
10							
11							
12							
13							
14							
15							
16							
17							
18							
19							
20							
21							
22							
23							
24							
25							
26							

PROBLEM

CHECK REGISTER

DATE	CK. NO.	PAYEE	ACCOUNT DEBITED	POST. REF.	OTHER ACCOUNTS DEBIT	ACCOUNTS PAYABLE DEBIT	PURCHASES DISCOUNT CREDIT	BANK CREDIT

PROBLEM

CHECK REGISTER

	BANK CREDIT	PURCHASES DISCOUNT CREDIT	ACCOUNTS PAYABLE DEBIT	OTHER ACCOUNTS DEBIT	POST. REF.	ACCOUNT DEBITED	PAYEE	CK. NO.	DATE
1									
2									
3									
4									
5									
6									
7									
8									
9									
10									
11									
12									
13									
14									
15									
16									
17									
18									
19									
20									
21									
22									
23									
24									
25									
26									